W9-ASG-163

19-33

NOV 1971
RECEIVED
OHIO DOMINICAN
COLLEGE LIBRARY
COLUMBUS, OHIO

HEAVEN IN THE HOME

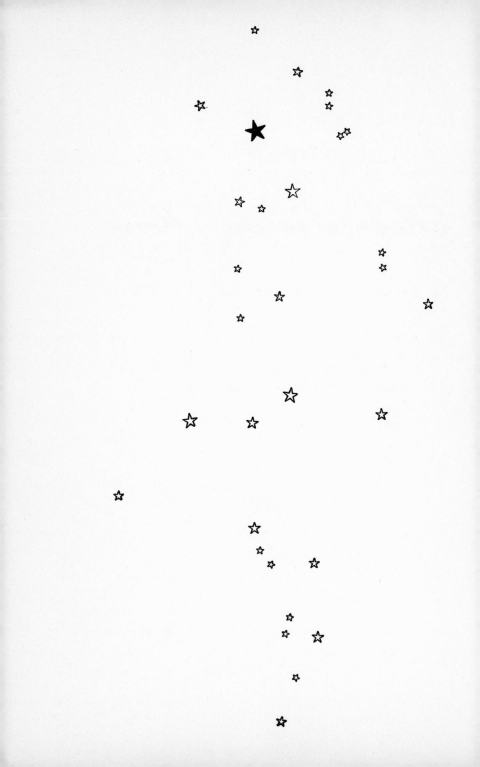

Heaven in the Home

by CHARLOTTE EDWARDS

★

HAWTHORN BOOKS, INC. *Publishers* NEW YORK

© 1959 by Charlotte Edwards. Copyright under International and Pan-American Copyright Conventions. All rights reserved, including the right to reproduce this book, or portions thereof, in any form, except for the inclusion of brief quotations in a review. All inquiries should be addressed to Hawthorn Books, Inc., 70 Fifth Avenue, New York City 11. This book was manufactured in the United States of America and published simultaneously in Canada by McClelland & Stewart, Ltd., 25 Hollinger Road, Toronto 16, Canada. Library of Congress Catalogue Card Number 59-6877.

FIRST EDITION
May 1959

814.54
E26 h

For

MOTHER
who straightened the curtains
and set the shades even,
and walked bravely out the front door,
not looking back.

78532

FOREWORD

We are all together in this age.

Some of us are very young.

Some of us are in the warm productive space of life.

Some of us are noting the first gray in the hair.

Some of us are moving more slowly, a little achy in the bones.

Some of us lie quietly, most of it done and over.

You and I, and all the others like us, no matter the number of years set upon us, have one need we all share. It is as compulsive as love or food or water.

That is a place to look.

We are tired.

We are afraid.

We do not know where to look.

When we glance back we see gray phantoms of Wars and Depressions.

When we look forward we see the horrible mushroom, and pray that it will never be more than a phantom.

The backward look, and the forward, all too often turn rancid the taste of the moment, the here and now.

Yet, it need not be.

If we find a place to look.

More—if we find a *way* to look.

Take the time with me, will you? and the thinking and a little of the emotion, and help me search for that place.

When we find it, let's use the seeing eye, the feeling heart, the changed view, the revision of attitude.

Come on, let's go home.

Home, they say, is where you hang your hat. Home is an abode or residence, or the dwelling place of a man and his family.

More widely, home is where you hang your heart. To be at home means, "to the uttermost, closely."

That is what makes the difference, doesn't it?

Near enough to touch. Unexplored.

You can look to each other. You can look downward to your children. You can look outward to your world. And inward to yourself.

Will you try with me?

Together, you and I, we swing our heads slowly around, examining it all, from the first tentative beginnings, to the present, and beyond.

Together, we search for new vision, deeper insight, greater courage and richer security.

Together, perhaps, we can cherish the moment for what it is—to the uttermost, closely.

CONTENTS

Foreword

PART ONE ☆

☆

☆

LOOKING TO EACH OTHER

☆

☆

CHAPTER ☆ ✦ ☆

THE CINDERELLA STORY

☆

Almost a year ago a letter came to my desk. It was written in black ink in what is often labeled "a round and childish hand." It came shortly after a story of mine appeared in a magazine, about two ill-assorted and very young lovers.

It was a nice letter, from a girl in the Midwest, sixteen years old, who was sensitive and open to the little story I had told.

Inside the folded sheet of compliments she had written a small poem.

"Song for April," it was called.

It read:

Because I walked with April, hand in hand,
Where moon and fog played tag through mist and light,
I understand the language of the night
That talks with splash of waves against the sand.

13

Though all the moons of April someday wane,
And every springtime mist dissolves with sun,
Last night I walked alone with April rain,
And ocean, moon, and fog and I were one.

I recognized the girl from the Midwest. I was sensitive to the little poem. Reading it, *I* was again sixteen a far time ago. I walked along the beach of one of the Great Lakes on a day of birds and sunshine and white sand. I walked through the woods of that lake's peninsula on a day of shimmering rain.

I answered her note, returned the compliments and told her about another story, as yet unpublished. Then I went back to my work, regained my years and aged my viewpoint to normal.

Then, last week, there was another letter, the hand only a little less childlike, the ink still black.

Every month I look for your story. You said it was about a young marriage and I want to read it soon.

This wonderful thing has happened. I met a sailor. He says he's going to marry me. Imagine! A week after he first danced with me!

Mother doesn't like it one bit. I just turned seventeen and he is twenty-one and she says to wait and see.

We'll have to, which makes it sad, because he's off on a cruise and I won't see him for months. They seem like years.

Funny that I should tell you all this. But I feel as if I knew you and that you will understand, even if Mother doesn't.

Thank you for listening.

Cathy.

I haven't written to Cathy yet. I have carried her simple young words around in my mind for some time now. I have felt the responsibility of the fiction I create, as I never have before.

If I were to write to Cathy, fully, if these pages were the answer to her letter, I would say something like this——

It's a fine thing to feel as if you know a stranger, because in some rare way that stranger's thoughts and yours have met on the pages of a magazine.

What is even more wonderful, what I treasure, is that beyond a doubt, Cathy, the gap in our real ages is wider than that between you and your mother.

That is why I haven't answered you before.

Because, under the gray of my hair there is the sleek black it was when I was seventeen. Under the general laxness and wrinkles of my face, there is the firm taut flesh of the time when I was your age. Above all, under the years of my living, there is the poetic heart, the sweet vulnerable spirit, of your letter and your verse.

No matter how I talk and move and write and live, those things remain.

Well, that takes care of the gap in our ages. And it takes care of the gap in your mother's and yours, too. But your mother is right there. That makes it very different.

Cathy, will you listen to me? Knowing that underneath I am you, will you hear me out? Please?

I know why people cry at weddings!

I know how that very handsome sailor came into your life and looked at you. He spoke with authority and set some sort of seal upon you. Suddenly from now until the next time is forever. The moment you wake in the morning there is a picture in your heart. The letters fly between the two of you. Slowly, slowly the months close in. When they are done and through . . .

You can see him, can't you, Cathy? He pounds his heels down the sidewalk. He whistles maybe. He throws out a lariat of sweet sound to rope you in before he reaches you.

You can see yourself, can't you, Cathy? You stand tiptoe on the porch in your best dress with four crisp petticoats. Your hair is washed and brushed. Your lipstick is silky on your mouth. Your heart runs away with your breath.

You can feel him, too, can't you, Cathy? His hand reaches out first, then his arm, and later his nice young lips, fresh from the whistling, soft on your silky lipstick.

It's beautiful. It's good. It's right.

To stand at seventeen with a question all through you, and have the answer stride proudly to surround you, is beyond all saying.

It is the Cinderella story come true.

It is the Sleeping Beauty awakened.

Still—I know why people cry at weddings.

I know why your mother doesn't like it. She probably sheds a few tears during a marriage service, too.

Neither your mother nor I must handle roughly the question and the answer. But handle it we must, one way or another.

It is your mother's obligation to do this, because she brought you into the world.

It is my obligation, because you feel close to me, and because I wrote a story in the cause of young love.

How to say it? Even after all of the years of writing, of loving, of living, how to say it to you. . . .

First then—a question to ask yourself, Cathy.

When the Prince finally found Cinderella, what happened?

When he knelt before her and fitted that glass slipper (which is only a symbol of the way your sailor's arm will fit around you), when they rose together and went to the castle, surrounded by joy, by the certainty of happiness ever after— what happened then?

When the Prince found the Sleeping Beauty, and awakened her from her dream with his kiss (which is only a symbol, again, of your awakening, and mine, and your mother's and all women's)—what happened then?

What happened, in both cases, what happens next in all the *real* years and the *true* marriages, depends on two people, and two people only.

The boy and the girl.

The man and the woman.

Sometimes it is good and lasts and is happiness forever after.

Sometimes it is bad and shrivels or blows up, and leaves open wounds and scar tissue beyond mending completely.

Now, it doesn't matter whether you are seventeen or thirty-seven, Cathy. This is not a case of age, this love, this marriage. It can fail in the years of so-called wisdom just as easily as it can in the age of innocence.

It succeeds for reasons.

And it fails for reasons, too.

Don't be trapped by touch, Cathy.

So many marriages have failed because of that.

We stand, as girls, yes, and as boys, too, with a sort of wind against us. Inside, there is the turmoil and the reaching. There is the knowledge that we are half of something, the inborn instinct to become whole, to get on with a total sort of living.

This is a God-given thing. It is a miracle. From it stem all of us, back to the beginning.

So the wind is on us, and the drive is in us.

Then, somebody who looks fine and young and clean walks toward us. The touch is new. It is beyond anything we, untapped, remote within ourselves and waiting, have ever known.

Because we have read, heard and thought of love with our growing, the quick exultant conviction comes to us that we have found it. Found it with that touch.

Happiness ever after.

Cathy, you're a big girl now. I can speak to you freely. You read the articles. There are so many of them. Articles about failing marriages. About how to hold your husband. About all sorts of sex adjustments and intricacies.

They are all based on touch.

They are wrong, though. They are reversed. The accent is in the wrong place.

Perhaps your young sailor will be the love of your life. That would be wonderful.

But how do you know? Because of the way he looks and speaks? Because of the way you respond to his touch?

Cathy, believe this. In the world there are dozens of young men whose touch could thrill you equally.

You are ready. You are reaching. You are half.

This distinction, then, you must be very sure of.

You must not believe the Cinderella story. Or any of the ads. Or the movies. Or TV. Or even (traitor that I am) the stories in the magazines. Or any of the sources which say that love is a sudden blaze, a certain glance, a first touch.

There *can* be happiness ever after. But it must be earned.

To earn it, first of all, you must be sure that there is more than touch, than chemistry, than youth and halfness.

How can you be sure?

You can put a little age on your growing.

Once again, it doesn't matter whether this is teens or twenties or more. You must age together, you and the boy, so that you know each other way beyond any physical touch.

Some marriages are perfect physically—and are far from happy.

If they are not right physically, doctors will tell you that the malformation is seldom a physical thing in itself. It grows from a different source, a further adjustment.

When mental and psychological blockades are removed, when the way is cleared, the touch gains strength and fresh importance. It *adds to* the marriage and helps to heal it.

But, Cathy, touch alone, sex alone, is not enough. It never has been enough since the world began, nor will it ever be.

All touch, after a while, is shaped and influenced and geared to the overwhelming importance of the other things of love.

They are the things you seek right now. You cannot find them in a week, in a hurry, in a bright dazzle of touch and discovery.

A party deserves a slow bath, cologne, pin curls, your best clothes, dancing slippers, nail polish and makeup.

You can't get ready for a fine big party in a hurry. It takes a while to groom yourself.

Marriages fail, and very often, because we come to them slipshod and half prepared. We have not taken care of ourselves, found ourselves, prided ourselves. We do not know ourselves yet. We are an unknown quantity. An x.

Thus, we bring that x, the depths which are in us, to meet another unknown quantity, another x.

Very often it brings tragedy.

Take time then, Cathy.

When the Cinderella story is over, what about your poetry? What will become of that?

I don't mean that perhaps one day you might be a great and famous poet. But to write your verse, to feel it in the first place, makes you a certain kind of person.

With your sailor, will you have to bury this poetic feeling before it is really born?

Will he ever be able to walk with you into the delicate, lovely part of your mind where you hold that "Song for April" and all the other melodies which are singing silently there?

It takes time to find that out. Time for you to explore until you know about it, and yourself, and your sailor.

Suppose now, that you do take time. Suppose, now, that you're very sure that it is not touch alone, that it is steady and right and will last. Suppose your mother and I finally both agree that what you have is "the real thing."

No other person in all the world can make your full and complete happiness.

If they could, you would be gay all the day long with the joy and contentment that your parents wish for you.

If you go to marriage putting all of yourself into the solid simple basket of a man's mind and heart, you will be disabused and bitter in no time at all.

Young as you are, you have seen women around you who are like that. They speak disparagingly of their husbands. Their lips are a tight line. They sigh as they breathe. They snap at their children.

Young as you are, you must know that they were once as you, that it couldn't very well be the outside world that has made them bitter.

So it must be love turned sour and marriage turned bondage.

You've probably read this before, Cathy. But like so many things we read it slips through the mind like water through a sieve.

Give yourself an advantage they didn't have, Cathy.

Learn now that a man and a woman can walk hand in hand, all the distance, to the end of life.

But they can not walk the identical and same path.

They walk parallel roads. Always.

They are grateful, if they are wise, that the roads do not branch off away from each other. That they stay parallel, that they have the same direction, the same tendency.

There are paths and corners in a woman's mind which no man can ever explore, just as there are crannies in a man's thinking that you can never reach.

When you make your partner the sum of your world, and insist on turning all pockets inside out, you are apt to find the sum too small, to find too little change in your pockets to buy anything of value.

Accept this fact. Do not ask more than a man can humanly give.

Do not put upon him the terrible responsibility for your total happiness.

We can bring each other grave unhappiness in this life, Cathy. But it is impossible to give another person permanent happiness, complete and whole, like a sandwich on a plate.

Keep some of yourself, and respect some of him. Give both of you room to recharge your personal batteries and light your own ways.

A thing of youth, a thing which you must be very careful not to do, is ever to hurt love.

This sounds sentimental. But love has its own dignity. It has its own shine.

Unfortunately, the dignity is a cloak which may be snatched by a rough hand. The shine is like sterling silver. It tarnishes very easily if it is not polished.

Two people who love each other should build, should add to each other. This takes work, and trouble, and something youth seldom has—patience.

The first harsh words are, somehow, no matter how quickly forgiven, never forgotten. They beget their own reply. There is no building then. There is, instead, the subtracting process. The tearing down process is begun, brick by small brick. Until finally everything is torn and there is rubble where a growing home should stand.

It all comes down, Cathy, to a simple phrase.

You must bring your best self to marriage.

To be completely married, to start the home which will be more than just a house where two people live together, you must first of all not be trapped by touch.

You must wait until you are sure.

You must know yourself completely, what you are and what you have to give.

You must know the person who is to receive that gift as closely, and as largely, as you can.

You must not put upon him the burden for your whole happiness.

You must stock your own reserves for use in the times of aloneness.

You must not ask more than he has to give.

Having accomplished all these things, you must treat this love with respect and give it room to grow.

If you can do these things (and there are others, of course, but they come after the glass slipper, after the Cinderella story) nobody will say, "I cried at her wedding. I guess I had a premonition."

Those who cry at your wedding, your mother and I, and the rest, will be crying because we remember how it was. Perhaps, even, because we wish it had been that way for us.

Most of all, though, we will cry because we are plain glad for you.

We will be glad you waited and worked, discovered and tried. Glad that when you stand there, proud and white-laced, looking up at your husband's face, you know, in every way there is to know, that his is the *only* face you want to look up into.

Send me an invitation then, Cathy. I will come from any distance and with great pleasure.

☆

CHAPTER 2

ALWAYS THE UNEXPECTED

☆

My Aunt Helga used to say, "Always expect the unexpected."

My father said, "Never know when lightning will strike."

The teen-agers say, "That's the way the ball bounces."

Big city people shrug, "That's the way the fortune cooky crumbles."

They're all right, of course. They all say about the same thing.

What they say goes double in the home. Or triple or quadruple, as time passes.

You know this because you're living it right this minute—or you can remember it quite clearly.

We make neat little plans on paper, or in our minds. It's all clear. It's a fine straight road with a sure destination. It looks logical, broad, flat, and easy to walk on.

This we do from the time we are children.

We plan for Christmas. We plan for summer vacation. We plan for good grades. We plan for college. We plan for marriage. We plan for money in the bank. We plan for a family.

Funny thing. Each generation makes the same plans.

Funny thing, too. Each generation gets them knocked sky-high.

On the face of it, we would be a lot smarter if we lived from day to day and let the road and the destination reveal themselves a little at a time.

But we're human. We can't help it. With strong minds, wills, dreams, set upon our goals, we forge sturdily ahead.

When those goals are impeded, blocked, curved, changed, time after time, by circumstances over which we seem to have little or no control, along come the frustrations which call for constant adjustments.

We don't have a thing to say about many of the events that change our lives, but we do have a great deal to say about those adjustments.

Or, as some anonymous old gambler put it, "I ain't able to say nothin' about the cards dealt out to me. But I can play 'em as I see fit."

Well, then.

When the Cinderella story has come to its logical conclusion, the living begins.

It begins with the plans, of course.

It gets sidetracked away from those plans, of course.

Remember? It starts out all right.

Your husband seems so big and strapping. He carries you over the doorstep of your new home with no more effort than if you were a bolt of lightweight silk.

You're both working.

You get up in the morning and laugh and talk while you

bathe, dress and fix breakfast together. You turn the key in the front door. Maybe you pat the doorknob and say to yourself, "I'll be back, little house. We'll be back."

You take your workaday orders and make your living. It's all new and fresh and exciting.

There's money enough for all of the little time payment books. It's fun to share the dishes and the washing, and to get down on your knees on Saturdays to make the kitchen and bathroom floors shine.

Saturday afternoons you are lazy together, lying out in the sun in the backyard or sitting with the reading you like best before the fire, depending on the season, knowing that steaks are waiting for dinner.

Sundays you visit your families, to be royally fed and fêted, or you take a ride or go to the beach. But wherever you go, you come back together. Always in the back of your minds is the fresh repeated joy of your own door to close, your own lock to turn, the delicious, unbelievable intimacies which marriage has provided.

Always in the back of your minds, too, is the knowledge that things are getting paid for. And some day, the two of you will be three. With money in the bank!

Are you a step ahead of me? Of course. One night you come home from work. One of you is crying, the other is frowning. Both of you sigh—and there you are.

The money is not in the bank. The honeymoon is barely over. The payment books are as thick as a deck of cards to be fanned in our hands.

The baby, the planned-for-someday-when-it's-the-right-time baby, doesn't know how to read plans and budgets. It has only one idea in its embryo mind. And that idea is to join the family, get into the act, begin to live.

Road block. Detour. The beginning of many.

This is just one off-trail, one big log to climb over, one sudden curve which blots out your vision of the road ahead. This is one out of many.

Always the unexpected.

How ready are you to face it? Will it tear down or enhance your marriage?

You've had some practice in the small things.

Some people wake up bright and whistling in the morning, long before the alarm clock clangs. Others cling to the pillow as if it were the only friend in the world.

Some people are sleepers, and often, sleepers snore. Some are awakers and the sleeper's snores drill into their ears and nerves.

Most marriages seem to consist of one sleeper and one awaker. Something to do, possibly, with opposites attracting.

There is plenty of room for conflict here, and Cinderella never considered such a thing, did she?

Take television.

Every night it flashes boxing and wrestling. Every night it offers plays and music.

Take food.

Some people eat nothing but meat, potatoes and vegetable for dinner. Other people love casseroles and big tossed salads.

Take words.

Some people are full of them—"Let's talk, dear."

Others pull into themselves—"What about?"

Any young couple in love will pooh-pooh these small discrepancies. The big overpowering thing which has sparked between them, pulled them together, tied them with gossamer steel threads, laughs at the idea that sleeping, waking, eating,

TV, talking or silence could possibly dampen that spark or break those threads.

But they have. Time and rueful sad time again, they have.

Alone at work, alone at home, resentment about small differences piles up. When the first quarrel comes, all of the small things are waiting, with tiny claws sharpened, to get their chance to come scratching into the light.

They do, too.

And two people are hurt. And love is hurt.

Here then, searching for a place to look, you can try first of all to discover a way to look.

In all of the little things.

When you were a child, remember how it was? The first time you went out to play, you didn't want the neighbor children to touch your new doll, or your new toy car. You wanted it for yourself.

When you first played games, remember how it was?

You wanted to be the leader, the teacher, the boss. You wanted to decide the game and tell the rules and have all the rest of them do as you said.

When you went to school, remember how it was?

You wanted to be the one to spell out *c-a-t* before anybody else could, or stay after school to help teacher clean the boards, or stand up in front to say the poem you learned at home.

In all of us, from those early days, there is the desire to keep it for ourselves, to rule the roost, to win the race, to shine and be the special one.

But the outside world felt the same way, too. So what did you do?

You learned to share. You learned to take turns. You

learned to hush up and let another student show off once in a while.

Those are all very basic, simple, young thoughts which we all have punched into us when we are, ourselves, basic and simple and young.

Why then, when we marry somebody in a positive welter of love and start a close life with a member of the opposite sex, do we so quickly, so thoroughly, so easily forget those simple premises?

It has something to do with love, in a subtle reverse order. We play a subconscious game to prove to ourselves, or have proven to us, how much the other person loves us—how far he will go in self-denial to prove that love.

This is, certainly, a feminine characteristic. It is probably also a masculine one.

If your husband will give up his pet golf game to go shopping with you, you will know he loves you more than himself.

If you will go bowling when you really want to go dancing, your husband will realize the depths of your affection.

So begins, with very small daily events, the juggling for the balance of power, always colored by emotion, never rational, which chips the very bottom bricks upon which marriage is built.

So begins an attitude which can grow to enormous proportions and break down every wall in the new unpaid-for home more quickly than any catastrophe.

There has to be a balance, certainly.

But not a balance of power.

A balance of love.

It is taking turns.

It is letting the other partner shine.

It is saying, "Look here, you play golf Saturday, and Sunday take me to that romantic movie and hold my hand. All right?"

Now, let's get back to that unexpected baby, that really big curve in the road.

If you have developed your attitude in small things enough, if you have been willing to give in at least every other time, it won't be so hard to face this new, this bigger, challenge.

Your husband must, first of all, pull himself together and try to see how it is with you.

You're young. You're pretty. You have always moved freely, light as a feather on the dance floor and around the house. You are used to people at work, and nothing more important to decide about than how to cut your hair or what to fix for dinner. Nothing larger to fear, let's say, than that early fear that perhaps the boy you loved wouldn't find you attractive enough to propose.

Now suddenly, the sky has fallen in.

Your feet hurt. Your dresses don't fit. Your waistline disappears and your stomach isn't flat. There are no people to work with. You are dizzy and ill.

And above all, there is that big dark strange place where you will go alone, a place of fear and pain, looming six months away, then four, then three, then two.

Whatever small sacrifices your husband has made in the name of love have just been dry runs to those he must make now.

There is a big reason for making this his turn. All of the years ahead, and your feeling for him, are going to depend on what he does for you now.

Now is no time for balance of power. Or even balance of love. Now is the time for loving, loving in a sense that your husband, young as he is, inexperienced as he must be, has never divined.

He must, first of all, not resent this intrusion, this change, this angling away from what he had planned.

You will adjust to the idea sooner than he. That is female and primal and instinctive. Even before your baby moves, an inside butterfly, maternity will have translated your discomfort into pale pink buntings and small knitted socks.

Not so with your man's instincts. Not so at all.

This unseen, unmade, half-done intrusion can be pictured by him, if he tries at all, as a good-sized boy playing catch on the sand lot or mowing the lawn when Dad is tired. He can see, if he tries, some of the friendly memories of his own youth, his own father.

But he can't see the baby.

He sees you. He sees the changes in you. He feels the withdrawal, the untouchable place in your mind. And it is not easy. Never easy.

But if the new home is to be what it can be, he tries.

He is tender. He is unasking, especially in extra tasks, in clean shirts, in fussy meals. Particularly in physical demands. He awaits your overtures. He gauges your moods. He gives you, perhaps for the first time in your relationship, just a friendly solid shoulder to lean against, a soft undemanding kiss.

Above all, he is there. Whenever you turn to look at him, whenever the sudden panic of the unknown assails you, he is there. To touch for a moment. To ask a question of. To walk around the block with. To reassure.

This is important. Never, until you are very old and your charm is gone, your physical attractiveness faded, will you need the reassurance you do during those long, yet tightening, months.

You cannot be sure, until now, that he didn't marry you because you smelled sweet, or had soft hair, or kissed nicely, or could dance better than any other girl in the crowd. You can't be sure that his love goes beyond your skin, your prettiness and your youth.

Until he shows you.

Many a divorce after ten years of marriage had its first sharp seeds planted in these months.

Yes, certainly you are special. Certainly you feel different. But that does not absolve you from your portion of understanding during these months, either.

You look at your husband.

There was a house, an obligation, and you were both working for it. Now the pay check is only a little more than half what it was.

There was a young man, all of his energies going forward into his job, mind cleared for action by the happy evenings and nights of laughing and loving with his bride.

Now there is a young man with a mind beginning to be cluttered by pressures, by the knowledge that he is responsible for you there at home—for your food, your lodging, your hospital bills, your baby.

Not yet "our" baby. That comes later, and with more growing.

You see that here is your husband, uncertain in the same areas that you are uncertain. If you look carefully you can see that he, too, is bearing this child. In a different way, one that he doesn't even realize perhaps. But bearing it with his manhood, with standing up to an unexpected situation, with offering his shoulder to a heavier burden.

You see that he feels trapped in a different way, but in just as tight a trap.

So, you practice, for the first time, a little of the maternal tenderness you will expend so lavishly on the new baby.

You avoid talking constantly about yourself and the expected child. You keep the routine of the evenings nearly what it was. You do the best you can with your changing form. You draw his attention to your hair, your makeup, the brightness and normalcy of your smile.

You, in short, and with a little feminine subtlety, assuage your husband's unexpressed fears. You let him see, as clearly as you can, that nothing is changed in your feeling toward him. You do this as surely as later you will reassure your first child when a second baby comes into the home.

Women know, instinctively, that there is love enough to go around. Women know it can spread comfortably from person to person, like a store of blankets in the cupboard big enough to add to every bed in the house on a cold night, even when company comes.

Children and men are not always so sure of this. They sometimes have the feeling that love is like candy in a paper bag, weighing only a specified amount. They sometimes feel that every scoopful of love which is given to another human being is a scoopful which lightens their own portion.

This is not so. Love begets love. Love increases by the act of loving.

I said this once in a novel. And it has been proven deeply to me many times since.

I wrote, "Love is not a penny to be hoarded like a miser's gold, until it adds up to a secret hidden fortune. Love is to be spent, recklessly, lavishly. Love is a muscle that grows sturdy with its own use. It is an arm stretched outward and down, to encircle, to protect."

If love is used that way, it can stretch to far distances in universality and empathy for all the world.

But we are not concerned here with such a bigness, such a breadth.

We are concerned with love within the home, and how it can be used and strengthened, to grow by the proper use of circumstances beyond our control.

If, in the easier times, you have learned to share, to give and take, to think of the other before thinking of self, then when the going turns strange, rough and frightening, you can step out of yourself—not a great distance, just a little—and understand your partner.

When the unexpected takes the form of a baby, that is a good event, with a reward to adjust to.

But all bolts of lightning are not so rewarding.

A man can lose a job, a woman can lose a child, illness can stab into the night, life can be filled with injustices too many to count.

A woman can stand, a man can stand, and search with panicked eyes for a place to look, because he or she did not anticipate the unexpected.

There will be no place to look in such times, except to each other.

In a way, the home is a cave. It is a lair, where we may hibernate through the cold times and the bad times.

Outside the cave, all sorts of terrors lurk. They are terrors which must be faced, even if not acknowledged, by each of us as we leave the cave daily to joust against the dragons of the world.

Sometimes we win, out there where everything happens. Sometimes we lose.

But the home, the cave, remains.

When we are the victors, it is a place to return to rejoicing, to share celebration, to bring our prides unashamedly.

When we are the vanquished, home is the only place anywhere that the wounds may be washed and cleaned and bound, that our lost courage may convalesce until it is strong once again.

The reason for this is that home is where love is.

That fact is too often forgotten by those who fight the battles. Sometimes it is forgotten by those who stay at home and wait.

In this modern time we don't like to say too much about love. We don't like to use any expressions with valentine lace around them. We're afraid of being labeled sentimental, even in our own minds.

Yet, the lonely ones, the thousands who have never found a person to love them, and whose homes are bachelor apartments or single rooms in women's hotels or who share a house with relatives, would be willing to talk about love all the day long. They would be willing to be called ridiculous. If only, when they came up a path, and reached for a key, the door would open first. If only somebody—anybody—would stand there waiting, with loving eyes.

It's a wonderful thing, if we hold still and think about it for a moment, to have someone care whether you get home safely or not, whether you are well or ill, even whether you are dead or alive.

It's a big world outside. Too big for any of us to bear, unless there is a small world inside somewhere and we are important in that small world.

Quite simply and practically, love should be a place where we can look and refresh our vision and our mind, as well as our heart.

Not in the Cinderella story fashion. Not that at all. Not a rosy cloud, full of floral perfume, changing all reality to some exalted euphemistic state.

Instead, we should be able to look to love, to our partner, without any pain at all. With only a sure knowledge that here, in this one place, no matter what goes on around us, there is true security, permanent safety.

So long as all is smooth and planned before us—no bumps, no hitches, no sudden swervings—this can be attained without too much trouble.

But comes the unexpected, the unanticipated, and it is no easy matter to look on love with a calm, sure expectancy of reward.

Thus, it becomes important, early in love if possible, to stop the jockeying for position, to love thy nearest and dearest neighbor as thyself, to unify and consequently strengthen. Then the world may be faced in double courage, with a double chance of winning out against it.

It all comes down to a simple phrase, an old one, to be looked at with new eyes.

"United we stand, divided we fall."

Many times, most all times, that double love can push out the fear, and wait out the situation, and work out the trouble —and the muscle of love is stronger for the next battle.

Because there will be a next battle.

Always the unexpected.

CHAPTER ☆ *3* ☆

WHITHER THOU GOEST

☆

When I was little, a long time ago, I used to sit on his lap and listen to Grandfather tell poems—long, sad, dramatic ones—and hum soft sentimental old songs.

My grandfather worked in a factory. He brought the smell of the factory in with him, a sort of steel tartness that I found pleasant. It was on his clothes and on his hands and in his pores, even when he was freshly washed and dressed.

I used to lean against him and sniff the strange odor. In my mind I could hear, through his humming, the noises of the plant.

My grandfather's head was as bald as an egg, with a perfect semi-circle of gray ruffled hair around it. He had a mustache which matched that sprouting hair, and he had very blue eyes.

He wore gray sweater coats, the kind that button down the front, and he had a very fat gold watch, which he pushed with his thumb to make the lid spring up and the face with its bold black numbers spring out.

When my grandfather came home, everything in the simple flat where he lived began to hum, too. The hot water in the teakettle seemed to wait for his step to shoot up its geyser. The salt-rising bread in the oven seemed to time itself to reach a golden brown just as he dried his hands. The creamed salt pork began to thicken. The potatoes almost mashed themselves. The green beans, which had stayed hard all afternoon over the low fire, suddenly were tender and crunchy.

The two-crust lemon pie was pricked out with his initial, a big *W* oozing sugary yellow.

My grandfather never had much money in the little tan envelope he spread out on the kitchen table after Saturday night's supper was finished. But all of his family was there to watch the proceeding, and to receive, if they merited it in his eyes, a speck of the change from the weekly portion.

It was a good and proud moment in the kitchen of the old flat. When it was over, and Grandma had received her house money, and the various little tobacco cans with their labels for monthly bills had taken their share, my grandfather jingled what was left in his hand.

He gave it a high jingle that shot the money up into the air and back, spinning and silver and looking like more than it was.

Then he put on his sweater coat and his cap. He patted everybody on the head, and bent to tickle the neck of the youngest with his mustache, and walked out of the door.

He sauntered down the street to the newspaper and confectionery store. He bought himself two tins of tobacco to last the week through, and a home town paper. He never got used to the fat city dailies. He talked to his cronies and wandered back home.

In his sweater pocket, the one which didn't hold the tobacco, was a striped bag of rock candy for my grandmother.

This she accepted, when he settled down in the rocker across from hers, with as much delight as if it were a five-pound box of chocolates with a big pink bow, and as much surprise as if he didn't buy her an identical bag every Saturday night.

Pay nights aren't Saturday night any more, as a rule. They're Friday.

The celebration of them doesn't take place around a kitchen table, either. It happens in a supermarket.

The parking lot of a supermarket on Friday night, and usually before dinner, looks like a carnival. Or like a huge bouquet of metal flowers, blooming and only partly paid for, on a great expanse of cement.

Inside, there is confusion. Children race up and down the aisles. Weary women chase after them. Weary men in flowered shirts or T-shirts or wilted white shirts push loaded baskets from counter to counter.

Supermarkets are happy to cash checks—or what's left of them after the groceries are paid for. At the checker's stand the whole family watches the register.

Dad pulls out his check.

Mom, peeking, whispers, "Gee, no overtime?"

Dad shakes his head as he writes his name on the back.

And sometimes Mom takes back the bottle of extra-large olives and the packets of candy bars.

Yes, Friday night is a big night at the supermarket. Mothers, fathers, children, TV frozen dinners, staples, "weekend specials," balloons floating, streamers flying, sometimes even soft music in the background.

A big night. In the liquor department especially.

"A man ought to get something for himself when he works like a dog all week."

A man gets a bottle.

The frozen TV dinners are really pretty good. But they can't compare with Grandma's salt pork.

The frozen pies are dandy, too. But there's no initial on them, except maybe *B* for boysenberry.

But no bottle could generate the glow that the two cans of tobacco, the home town paper, and the little bag of rock candy created.

Why is this?

There is an American institution today known as the Wednesday night fights. Have you ever taken a walk down the street on Wednesday night? Try it sometime.

From almost every house, in every community, all over the country, the announcer's voice cries out through the windows of a dim spotlighted living room.

"Kerner hurt Jalinko that time. A nasty one to the eye. Jalinko's eye is cut. It's cut badly. He's bleeding. Ten seconds left in the fifth and he's bleeding real bad now——"

Tiptoe up to that window and peek in—and there is to-day's man. He sits before the gray, active square. He's not slouched and dreamy as he often is on other nights. Not at all. He balances on the edge of his chair. His jaw twitches at the blows. His stomach tightens. His feet dance a little. His hands jerk from the chair arms.

Why is this?

Any night in the week, several hours each night, children sit before the television set and watch a gun snap out in a quick draw. They listen to the staccato snarl of bullets aimed at a live target. They fall off chairs in imitation of a death tumble. They battle going to bed before that seven-foot hero leaves the screen.

Sometimes Dad sits right there beside them, riding away in a lickety-split of dust. Sometimes Mom comes in from the kitchen, wiping a dinner dish rhythmically, as she, too, watches that big wonderful guy there on the screen.

Why is this?

Day after day, in the normal course of home life, children run to ask permission for something.

They run to mother.

She says yes, or she says no. Occasionally there's quite an argument.

Who settles the argument?

Dad?

Dad isn't home! Or he is busy doing some extra work he had to bring home. Or he is off on a special trip for the company. Or he just doesn't hear. Arguments are the order of the day, and he is adjusted to the noises of a busy office anyhow.

Why is this?

Not long ago a young man interviewed me on a television program.

He asked, "Do you believe, like the author Philip Wylie, the one who wrote *Generation of Vipers* and thought mothers were dangerous, that we are a country controlled by Momism?"

The question hit me suddenly—and hard.

I swallowed. I felt like a traitor to my sex.

I said, "Yes. Yes, I do."

He laughed at his cornering me.

"Why do you think there is so much Momism?" he threw at me next.

It came out without thinking. "Because there is too little Pop," I found myself snapping.

Even the studio audience laughed.

But I didn't laugh. I went home and thought about it, and I didn't laugh at all.

That was when I remembered my grandfather and those Saturday nights around the table after supper.

That was when I thought of the supermarket and those crowded aisles before supper.

That pay envelope was in my grandfather's hands. It was thin and small. It didn't take long to empty it, like a poor kid's Christmas stocking with only an orange and a stick of candy.

But Grandfather, himself, pulled out the bills which were the badge of his labor.

He, himself, decided which children deserved to be rewarded, and how much.

He, himself, gave Grandma what she needed, a hand-to-hand touch which said, in warmth and kindliness, "Thank you," and "You've earned it, my dear."

Then he, himself, knew his moment of freedom and tobacco. And he, out of the smallness of his largesse, remembered the woman who put a *W* on a two-crust lemon pie.

My grandmother was not an easy woman to live with after Grandfather died. I've always sort of understood why.

All right, so times have changed. Money doesn't mean much any more. Some men never see an amount in cash worth mentioning from year to year. It all happens by check, with the deductions already out—spoken for before it's received. There's never enough to go around anyhow, and what am I working so hard for?

It's a good question.

What any man is working so hard for is the expression on his children's faces when he gives them an allowance or a special treat, the expression of "Gee, Dad, for me?"

What any man is working so hard for is the look in his wife's eyes, the old-fashioned look that says, "You're a fine, big, strong man. You take good care of us. I don't know what we'd do without you."

When was the last time you saw children utterly enchanted by any gift? In words and looks and action?

When was the last time you saw a man take a deep breath and stand a little taller because his wife said or did or looked a way that added a few inches to his stature?

We'll get right down to it.

In the Book of Ruth, in the Bible, Ruth makes a statement. It's made to her mother-in-law, but no matter. What counts is that a certain combination of words came into being—and they have remained ever since.

"And Ruth said, Intreat me not to leave thee, or to return from following after thee: for whither thou goest, I will go; and where thou lodgest, I will lodge: thy people shall be my people, and thy God my God: Where thou diest, will I die, and there will I be buried: the Lord do so to me, and more also, if ought but death part thee and me."

In a strange unexplainable way, these days, within the family, we do intreat each other to leave us. We do return from following after. We do not go whither. Or lodge whither. Or make each other's people our people.

Above all, and most tragic, "ought but death" too often parts us.

Following after thee. Whither thou goest.

Now these are phrases which can mean more than one thing.

They can mean an actual move from place to place.

Our ancestors understood that well. The big brave young bucko wanted to see what was over the mountains and across the rivers, so he asked, "Will you come along, Nell?"

And Nell came along.

It's a good thing she did, too, or this country would be populated like "Reuben, Reuben I bin thinkin'," with all the women on the East coast and all the men in the West.

In wartime, there is once again an actual following.

Thousands of you can tell stories of living in one room, a Quonset hut or a barracks building, treasuring each day you were allowed to follow your husband before he was shipped beyond your reach.

Even in peacetime, women are gracious enough about a move from city to city if it will improve their husbands' job careers.

But there are other, less tangible, ways to follow—the most rewarding ways.

The secret of this kind of "whither thou goest" seems to be lost in our time. The meaning of "follow" seems to elude today's woman.

For the home, for the modern couple, this is a sorry, sad thing.

Women asked for it and they got it. Now they don't know what to do with it.

Emancipation. Equality. Freedom. A place in the sun.

Granted, they only wanted to walk arm in arm.

Admitted, they just wanted to be partners side by side.

But the whole thing got out of hand, somehow, and now women are the leaders.

46

Yes, they are.

They spend most of the money in the country. They pick out the clothes, the cars, the appliances. They decide what the children should do or not do. They become Den Mothers and sit on PTA boards and teach Sunday School. They have hobbies which sometimes turn out to be going businesses. They join together in women's clubs and bang tables with gavels and know all about parliamentary law. They hold down men's jobs on top of all this, and do them well and efficiently.

If that isn't being free and equal, and if it isn't more—being a leader—what is?

Yet, within all the range of my acquaintance, I can count on the fingers of one hand the number of women who are truly happy.

Now, why is this?

Let's go back to that husband we left watching the Wednesday night fights.

If we can find out why he watches them, perhaps we can find out why there are so few happy women.

Consider this.

There is no place in the civilized world where a man may use his fists. No place where he can battle it out, openly and courageously. No place where he can settle the tensions, the pressures, the frustrations, the insecurity, the injustices, the ignominious position he holds at work and, all too often, within his home. No situation which can be cleared up by a tightening of muscles, a clean throw, a battering, which will relieve him and, in some purely masculine way, cleanse his mind.

There should be no great mystery as to why men nowadays pulse with ulcers and die from heart attacks.

Men are not little boys, all cute feminine remarks to the contrary.

They are as straightforward as children, though.

It is against everything in their natures to turn inward upon themselves, to swallow the retort to authority, to eat of themselves in silence—just as it is foreign to them to sit down and try to analyze every move they make, as women so often do.

Yet, strangely, men have been forced to do just that.

Men today, watching those boxers, know a moment of identification. Of subconscious remembrance and satisfaction.

They know something else, too. Something they most likely never put into words.

They know a sense of loss.

Loss of what?

They don't know what.

Sometimes, without this knowledge, but instinctively trying to compensate for the unadmitted loss, men drink too much, or become involved with other women, or do any one of the much worse things that are daily publicized in the papers.

Some of them do. A very small proportion.

Most of them, quietly and in the most gentlemanly fashion imaginable, have retreated. Back and back from their original position as the leader and the head of the home, they have retreated, trying to recoup their losses at each step.

But they suffer a disastrous defeat.

They grow quiet in this defeat. Even at mixed parties the women toss the conversational ball. All too often the men congregate in small groups, coming alive only when they talk shop.

And there are few happy women. Very few.

There are many nags. There are many whiners. There are

many bosses. There are many chin-high brave ones. There are some disloyal ones, some outright shrews, some who speak of their husbands, and to them, as if they were dim-witted children.

But there are very few happy ones.

The man's loss is the woman's loss.

The modern wife, I deeply believe, is not happy, because she wants to follow—she needs to follow. And there is nobody out ahead of her to lead the way.

The modern wife, like a child, feels secure when she knows how far she can go before somebody says, "Here now, that's enough of that nonsense."

I do not believe that a woman wants, basically and instinctively, to hold the reins, to have complete charge of the home —often the money—with all the attendant annoyances, worries and problems.

She wants to help. She wants to share. But she never meant it to go so far that the major responsibilities fall upon her.

She wants to have somebody to look up to, to respect—an intelligence if not beyond her own, at least added to her own.

She wants, very much, to have somebody tell her confidently, "Don't you fuss about it, dear. I'll take care of it."

That is not a phrase that today's wife hears very often, if ever.

So, Mother, too, impelled by the same power as Junior, stands for a moment looking at the seven-foot Western hero— and tastes her own loss.

It is not a matter of fists, this loss, nor of guns and striding and flat-footed authority.

It is more subtle than that, this modern dilemma.

And who is to solve it?

Who is to make the first move to correct a situation which

has grown so slowly that most men do not realize the extent to which they have retired from the family, and most women recognize such retirement only as a feeling of general dissatisfaction and dislike of things as they are?

The wife will have to try. If she wants to. If she isn't so bound by the habit of being the voice of authority that she cannot lower her tone.

She can start with the children. She can even use them as an excuse, to herself and her husband.

Children need heroes other than pictured ones. Today's children often don't recognize the one real hero closest to them. They don't know he's a hero yet—until it is pointed out to them.

Taking a tip from Grandma, the children can be called in from play, to wash, brush and get ready for dinner because Dad will soon be home.

Taking a tip from Grandma, when they want to do or have something, they can go ask Dad. When they need homework help, Dad can be the one with the brains at arithmetic.

When Dad comes home, there can be a little of the conquering-hero-on-a-white-horse about the fact that he has charged the enemies all week long and won out once more against them.

Kids are haunted little creatures. If their parents read a lot, they like books. If their parents swear, they swear. If their parents argue, they argue. If their parents yell, they yell.

And if their mother clears the hour of Dad's homecoming and shows that he is a specially welcomed and loved arrival, they will get the idea in no time. They will treat Dad with a similar respect and affection.

So we come at last and again to the woman and the man.

It won't be easy and it won't be quick. Women have taken

a long time to reach their exalted, if often unwanted, position. In many cases it has simply been willed to them from the generation of the first suffragette.

They don't want to lose, in any way, what is good about their freedom. But they don't have to make a spectacular slide back to fainting and meekness.

They can reach for a hand. They can turn to the man they married in love, and consult him—about everything.

They can make him feel tall, and strangely rested, by being concerned with what has happened to him during the day. They can share his interests outside of working hours. They can give him an almost forgotten warmth by showing whose side they are on when he has been badly treated—or even just thinks he has.

Once it is started, it comes naturally, this bowing a little to the husband's opinions, waiting to let him speak once in a while, letting him lead—and following after.

A warning, though.

It won't be easy.

Dad isn't used to all of these distractions. He will be impatient with the calls upon his time, his opinions, his suggestions, his love. He has walked a lonely path for a long while. He's very apt to be annoyed and confused at first when the traffic begins to clog that road.

But one day he's going to realize something.

He's going to realize what Grandfather knew without ever thinking about it.

He will be driving home one night—and it will hit him. An old forgotten excitement to hurry, hurry home. To find out what the boy timed in swimming and if the girl passed in algebra. Above all, to hear what his wife has to say about that special job the boss passed on to him because he was the only one the boss trusted.

He'll know, that moment, that he is important to his wife and his children. He'll know he's not just a meal ticket. He won't ask, "What am I working for?" He'll know he's important as a person.

More than that. As a man. The man of the house.

More still, the head of the house.

It's worth any woman's trouble.

P.S. My grandmother's teeth weren't very good. Rock candy set them on edge. But every Saturday night, she emptied that little bag.

P.P.S. My grandmother's recipe for two-crust lemon pie is printed below. You just dot in the initial with a regular kitchen fork—big!

TWO-CRUST LEMON PIE

For the crust, take two scant cups of flour. Add a teaspoon of salt. Sift over two-thirds cup of shortening and cut in well. Add four tablespoons water, one at a time, and mix lightly but well, with fork.

Roll gently (a light hand for crust always), add filling and top crust, and bake in moderate oven (350°) till golden brown.

FILLING

1½ *level* cups sugar
2 large eggs, beaten
Juice of 1½ lemons
Stir until creamy.

CHAPTER 4

"THE BEST IS YET TO BE"

During the War we lived with an old couple, sharing their home and kitchen privileges. The little old lady weighed about ninety pounds. The old man had once been tall, but he was bent over and shaky and his legs were wrapped in bandages.

They owned a simple gray-shingled house and an ancient car for which they couldn't get a license, and every drawer and cupboard in the house was filled with small treasures they had squirrelled away. Both of them were practically confined to the circumference of their house, the back yard and the grocery store half a block down the street.

They had lived together a long time, those two. They had raised three children, given them the best educations, permitted them to scatter all over the country, were proud of their seven grandchildren, and didn't ask anything of anybody.

Except of each other.

Oh, they nipped at each other sometimes.

Especially when the cherry tree was hanging heavy.

That's when Elgar insisted on picking every last cherry. He got out the ladder from the garage, and that was a major project. He set it up firmly against the tree, and that was a second great effort. He tied a big pan around his neck, with a piece of rope, and that took a while, too, because his hands were swollen and slow.

Then he climbed that ladder and hid his face among the leaves and the shining, deep crimson clusters of cherries. That was the greatest effort of all.

The first few hours Ella didn't mind. She got all the pots and kettles out (an awesome accumulation) and set them around the kitchen. She measured the hoarded sugar, rations for months. As Elgar brought the cherries in, she pitted them, washed them and started to preserve, to can, to make jam and jelly.

Scattered all over the kitchen were the jars, glasses, pans. Boiling on the stove were the concoctions just beginning, the ones half-cooked and the ones ready to drain and pour.

The sun was hot and the weather was muggy in the town during the season when the cherries were ripe. The kitchen was Hades with a linoleum floor. Ella's white hair turned flat and scrawny. Her busy little feet slowed hour after hour. Her face gleamed with perspiration in every wrinkle.

But still the cherries came. Buckets of them.

That old man with bandages on his legs, perched insecurely on the ladder, his head hidden in the greenness up there, was a demon!

All the first day, all the second, all the third, up he went,

54

and there he stayed, and down he came, and in went the cherries to the kitchen.

By the end of the second day Ella looked completely undone every time he kicked the screen with his foot.

"There's no keeping up with you," she cried. "Let the birds have a few. Give them to the neighbors. I'm tons behind you."

He shook his head and peered at her over his glasses and put on his professorial air.

"Waste not, want not," he admonished.

And back to the tree he went.

It was a hard time in the old gray house. It was a hard time in the old marriage.

"Damn the cherries," Ella said in the middle of the third afternoon. "And damn you," she added, whispering.

I heard it. I grinned.

But it bothered me just the same.

I was pretty young during the War. It seemed to me that by the time you reached your seventies, there ought to be a glorious sort of serenity in marriage, a calm and complete understanding, a perfect give and take.

And no cursing! Especially from the pure lips of such a dear white-haired little old lady.

When the cherries were all gone from the tree, when every last one had been brought in by those swollen hands and those shuffling feet, when all the sugar had been used (and five pounds of mine, too) they asked me to look.

They stood together in the kitchen and waited for me to admire.

It was an admirable sight, that you can believe.

All the flat surfaces—the sink, the stove, the breakfast nook, all cupboards and the dining room table—were bedecked and packed with shimmering jars and glasses. Each one of them had a white flag pasted on its front. Inscribed in precise shaky letters were the date, the kind and the family name.

There was more than a family of ten, simply crazy for cherries, could have managed to do away with in two years.

I helped them carry the abundance down to the storage cellar. Elgar unfastened the padlock and swung the door wide. There, from floor to ceiling, were more jars and glasses than I had ever seen in a store.

I walked around, reading off the shelves as if I were in a library. The other older white flags dated back, some four years.

Ella watched me. She came over beside me. She looked proud.

"Only one more can of 1940," she said. "And then we can start on 1941."

I couldn't think of a thing to say.

I laughed about it, sometimes, when we talked over wartime experiences with friends.

But after we were away from that simple gray house, whenever the cherry season came along, I used to stop for a minute. I used to say a little prayer that Elgar was still climbing up into that tree. And that Ella was rushing and perspiring, and maybe even cursing softly, to keep up with those silver bubbles on top of the red richness in all those pans.

I could not quite forget the way the two of them looked, down in the storage cellar with one overhead light cutting across the pride on their faces, when the last jar was put away.

I always remembered the way they forgot me, and turned to each other, and reached out simultaneous hands, and smiled almost identical smiles.

"Well," Elgar said.

"Yes," Ella echoed.

I still think of them at cherry time, although they have been dead for a long time.

I realize now that the cherry tree was a challenge and a symbol. I hope very much that they managed to meet that challenge every year until the very last.

It was something they accomplished together in years so circumscribed that there wasn't much they could do any longer.

Elgar set himself to manhood and danger when he climbed that tree. He urged Ella on, as he must often have urged her through hard, busy, younger times.

And Ella kept up. She struggled and was angry and deplored his masculine stubbornness. But she kept up. And worked with him. And created something with him.

When it was done, they shared the feeling of victory and were close in the thing they had managed to do—despite age, and aches, and pain, and weather.

When they had stored the shining new jars, they looked at all the hundreds of jars, back four years. I wouldn't be a bit surprised if that magnificent and frightening accumulation wasn't their guarantee of mortality.

"Waste not, want not"—and whoever was going to die and leave all those cherries to be eaten, all that jam to be spread?

Those two words, "Well" and "Yes," were an autobiography, a biography, a novel, a textbook.

They were, "Grow old along with me! The best is yet to be, The last of life for which the first was made."

To grow old in marriage is to grow old, many, many times, in wisdom. It is to hold—represented in a cherry tree or some other symbol—all experience, all effort, all victory.

57

For us to experience here, in words, the total of things that went into an old, worked-on marriage like Ella and Elgar's, would furnish any number of volumes.

But the mileposts they shared can be talked about and thought about. Perhaps trying to see what they must have accomplished will help our own marriages—no matter what their stage of present development—to fruition and maturity.

Even Ella and Elgar, for instance, couldn't have been spared the day, or the evening, or the night, when they looked at each other and said, "Is this all? Is this all there is to it?"

The house was the same, the dinner was fine, the baby was tucked in and quiet.

But Elgar, or Ella—it doesn't matter which—looked up from a book, or across a room, and the thought came, "Is this all?"

Wake up, dress, wash, eat breakfast, work all day, wash, eat dinner, find some small entertainment to fill the free hours, go to bed.

"Is this all?"

The hopes, the dreams—the wonderful way it was always going to be—were diminished. It was all finished and done. Signed, sealed, delivered. Forever after, amen. The same deadly routine.

Elgar fell asleep on the davenport. Ella stared at him bubbling his small snore. Where is his specialness? she thought. Where is his magic charm that seemed to make him different from all other men?

Perhaps Elgar looked across the breakfast table, and his wife turned her head up, frowned. He stared, then looked away in embarrassment, as if he had stepped by accident into a strange room.

All right. It happened. Every day it happens. It's universal.

"The honeymoon is over."

Natural, yes. But it still hurts.

When it happens, what is done about it makes all of the difference.

Did Ella, do you suppose, spend that strange day telling herself that she had made a mistake, that she was married to a man who didn't have a word to say to her when he came home?

Did Elgar hold that little picture of his wife with her frown, no lipstick and the baby's oatmeal stuck on her chin, in his mind? Did he, perhaps, contrast it with Miss Quiggle, fresh as a daisy, as she took his dictation?

Those aren't big disloyalties. They're small ones. But they can be the beginning of all separation.

Something must be realized, between two people.

If you have ever studied hard, really trying to learn, you know that you go forward quickly and well for a long time. Then you hit a plateau.

If you have ever dieted, you know that the pounds will slip off quite neatly for a while. Then weeks go by and you starve, and you can't lose an ounce. You've hit a plateau.

It's like that in marriage.

It glows and seems important and getting somewhere. You feel close, allies against any danger, part of each other's thoughts.

Then, on a breath, and for no reason at all, it falls apart and you are alien.

You have hit a plateau.

A plateau is a flat place perfect for resting, for moving slowly, for getting breath before another hill looms ahead.

In order for any real emotion to subsist, there have to be times of no emotion at all—of coast, of ebb.

For those who worry about such times, and try to do something about them, real trouble can develop.

For those who are willing to rest, to coast, to know that absence of emotion is healthy and natural, the richness will build up again, slowly and steadily. Just as sleeping recreates strength, one fine day or one fine evening, or one fine night, you, like Ella and Elgar, will look across the room at each other. And it will be as it used to be, or even better.

You will be hungry for sharing, and touch, and talk, both rushing to tell the things seen and done and felt in that far private country, where the rope was slack and you walked a flat way by yourselves.

Another milepost (in a worked-on marriage like Ella and Elgar's) is compromise.

Perhaps COMPROMISE should be written in capital letters, followed by an s. Many small ones make up the big one, and they're all important.

There is a compromise with life itself. This is an individual matter for all of us. But when two people live intimately together under one roof, it becomes a dual compromise.

It goes back to the Cinderella story, the happiness-ever-after fable, which has twisted so many lives.

Nobody is going to be happy ever after anything.

No life is going to be perfect.

No love is going to be perfect.

Ella and Elgar found that out. And so will you.

This is such a ridiculously basic premise that it seems silly to write it down at all.

But in the hidden part of their minds, as in yours, it sat. The big hope. The feeling of being different and special. The wanting to walk from day to day and place to place in a glow of joy.

When the glow of joy turns gray and dulled, if there is no compromise with love, there is only blame for the other partner.

You see, we forget so easily that nobody else can furnish us with happiness.

Eventually, though, a marriage like Ella and Elgar's, good, mature, solid and lasting, doesn't forget this. It admits that love is sometimes a thing, an emotion, of great vitality and intensity.

It also admits that love is sometimes a knife, a needle, a pain in the mind. It is not easy to love in the full sense, to submerge ourselves, even partially, by admitting another person's importance to us.

It also admits that love is sometimes no emotion at all—that plateau we were speaking about.

All of these admissions are compromises. Each of them is hard to accomplish. Each adds to the quality of a marriage which makes it last.

Compromise in time of disagreement, a compromise which touches pride, touches bitterness, was probably the hardest-won of all for Ella and Elgar.

With children, you try never to take a stand unless you can back it up. You never go out on a limb, unless it's strong enough to carry your weight.

If this is important with children, think how much more vital it is in marriage.

Yet it is forgotten time after time.

If you demand an ultimatum, you're very apt to get it.

If you make an ultimatum, you're very apt to have to stick with it.

This is getting yourself out on a limb with a vengeance.

If, in a storm of protest, injured feelings, hurt pride, Ella

61

stalked out of the house and went somewhere else, it couldn't have been easy to get back into that house.

Other people, outsiders, knew about it, sympathized with her perhaps, listened to her. They, in turn, being human, told others.

When, and if, Elgar's young hand was stretched out from that house to her, it was a long way back on a shaky limb to reach his hand.

Some people never make it, and a marriage is finished.

The lasting couple learn to avoid that limb entirely. They let a little time go by. They let a little silence fill the air. They let the other one find his or her way back, in quiet, in thoughtfulness, in love.

They, in short, stay with the trunk of the tree, their love for each other. When the storm is over, the tree may show a scar, or a heavy burled knot, but it will go on growing.

Every marriage as old as Ella and Elgar's has known the Heroic Gesture.

One time or another something so big, so real, so fearful, must have struck, that a big gesture was needed to keep the marriage from collapse.

One may have been unfaithful. The other may have forgiven.

The wife may have given up and gone home to mother. The husband may have followed on his knees and begged her to return.

We could make quite a list, but the newspapers do that for us when they report the causes for divorces.

The Heroic Gesture gouges into the ego like no other form of love.

It may not be so hard to make initially, but you have to live with it all the rest of your lives.

It's not so amazing for a soldier to dash out under fire and throw the grenade that will free his group from a sniper.

It is more unbelievable, and braver, for a soldier to drag an injured companion, mile after mile, hour after hour, unendingly, through enemy fire.

It is good, but not surprising, that Ella or Elgar could forgive—in a sudden excess of courage, emotion, need—the infidelity, the cruelty or the shame of a truly repentant partner. Warmth, tenderness, pity, love itself rise to the occasion in a big blend.

What was hard, what took real courage, was that, once forgiven, once understood, the gesture had to be lived out day by day. It had to be buried, hidden, forgotten.

Never, in all of the years after, could they drag it from its hiding place in times of small resentments, to crack like a whip across the heart of the person forgiven.

This is hard.

A plane heading across the ocean reaches a point of no return. This means that it is just as far a journey back to the starting point as it is ahead to the destination.

It is a dangerous place for a plane.

It is a dangerous place for a marriage.

Every lasting marriage, even Ella and Elgar's, must reach its point of no return. It can then go on to a good conclusion because of this very point.

At this point as much has been invested in the marriage as can be invested in the years still remaining. As far back to the beginning, as it is ahead to the end. A time to take stock, to think twice—and carefully.

Unfortunately, this point of no return in matrimony generally coincides with what is known as a dangerous age in life

—the middle years, the time of restlessness, the days when the house is clear of children.

In the middle years the hours hang heavy, the evenings are slow and dull. There doesn't seem to be much for two people to say to each other, after years of noise and excitement and interruption.

But Ella and Elgar got past this point. If you can, too, just a few miles, you'll be able, as they did, to make it to the airport.

You get past this point by looking back to the beginning. But not with wistfulness, not with wanting to start all over again with somebody else.

Rather, you look back as a stockbroker would, counting the investments which have already paid dividends, adding them all up, realizing what a small fortune there is already in your hands and how the stock might go up with the years if you can just hang on to it.

This is a bad time to sit down and count the ways that life has failed you, the ways your marital partner has failed you.

This is a bad time to look twice at the pretty girl, the handsome younger man, the cocktail glass, the sleeping pill.

This is a time for joint enterprise, for newness together, for surprising each other.

This is a refueling place, a shifting into second gear, knowing you are over the hump.

Ella and Elgar must have known this. Before they went ahead, they must have stopped for a while and looked around them. Looked back at the hard but beautiful path up which they had come. Looked ahead to the broad, sure, shared road down which they could go.

If they tried. If they tried together.

If you are fairly young, looking at a picture in the paper of

a Golden Anniversary couple like Ella and Elgar, it's hard to
believe that they have known the intimacies of sexual relationship.

They must have, of course, because all such anniversaries
are decorated with several children and a dozen or more
grandchildren.

The idea of sex always seems to be the original discovery of
the generation which has just learned about it.

Yet, that generation, if only it could or would listen to the
older ones—or if the older ones could fully, freely tell them—
would be eased and blessed to know what has gone before.

Any warm, human, thinking person who has been married
for a substantial and proud length of time could tell the
young ones a few helpful and rewarding facts.

Sex is good, but it is no good unless the way for it is cleared.
Cleared of resentments, cleared of mistrust. Cleared of shame.
Cleared of shyness. Cleared of selfishness.

Sex is good, but it is no good unless it is shared. Shared in
tenderness. Shared in attitude. Shared in completion. Shared
in friendliness.

Sex is good, but it is no good unless it is understood. There
is a basic difference between men and women, quite aside
from anything physical.

A woman must understand that to love her sexually is often
a man's apology for harsh words, for the difficulty of saying
tender ones, for not being able to give her all that he would
like.

This is not easy for a woman to comprehend. Too many are
imbued with the idea that a man loves them for a physical act
and not for "themselves."

In the straightness of a man's mind, there is not this dis-

65

tinction. If he doesn't love her, he doesn't want her—and it is as simple as that.

Sex is good, but it is not always intense.

In this age of ours—and this is our problem as it never was Ella and Elgar's—there is so much accent put upon the satisfaction to be gained from the sex act that it is like a physical counterpart of the Cinderella myth. Unless something shattering happens, unless there are fireworks, it is unsuccessful.

This just isn't so, as all the older ones can attest.

Times of intensity, in any lasting and worthwhile marriage, certainly occur. But sex can also be a gentle ease in times of weariness, a thing of comfort in times of unhappiness, a closeness when life has treated you both badly and there are no words to bring you close.

When it is intense, be glad. When it is not, be tender.

Sex is not love, but love always contains sex. Once again, we need the accent in the right place.

Love, tenderness, wanting to give, will open the door. As is so often true, the more you give, the more you get.

It's part of an intricate pattern, and all the colors are beautiful. It behooves you, as it behooved our long-married pair, to remember that.

So, Elgar looked at Ella and said, "Well," at the accomplishment they had shared.

She smiled back at him and said, "Yes."

Those two words, "Well" and "Yes," were an autobiography, a biography, a novel, a textbook.

Behind them, around them, shining more than any cherries in any crystal jars, there were the past and greater accomplishments which had brought them to that moment together, that "last of life for which the first was made."

The conquered disillusions, the compromises, the Heroic

Gestures, the sex, the point of no return, the understanding—those were the ingredients of their lives, their marriage.

Those are the ingredients of any marriage, of the years of looking to each other.

The way they are brought together, the fire which heats them, the hand which stirs them, like the proportions, are different with each man and each woman.

But it is good and heartwarming to know that every day in every newspaper, everywhere, there are pictures of white-haired couples like Ella and Elgar—two people who have taken these ingredients and brought them, after half a century of years, to a Golden Anniversary.

They deserve a medal!

And may you get one, too!

PART TWO ☆

☆

☆

LOOKING DOWNWARD

☆

☆

CHAPTER ☆ ◢ ☆

TEACH ME, SON

☆

Within all of us there are the lost years—the time of living when to feel was exquisite, sharp, of the moment.

These years are remembered with a brevity that is a snap of the finger, the flare of a match, the pull of a breath.

They go, like mist caught in the hands, a moth escaped, a sun cloud-dimmed.

Until we have a child. A child of our own.

This is what happened to me.

I woke slowly one day, fumbling through the fog of exhaustion.

In the back room the singing lilted up and down, light as only a very young child's voice can be light, pure and sweet and without a final cadence.

Between the singing phrases, there came a powerful change of tone, "Mommy, Mommy, Mommy!"

I lay in the bed and the darned sunshine was in my blinking eyes. Every worry in the world was in my littered mind. My head ached. My corn hurt. And the coffee was yet to be made.

I stumbled from the bed and worked my way painfully into the back room. I didn't look directly at the uplifted, eager face.

I said, petulantly I suppose, "Why in the world do you have to wake up so early?"

"It's morning time." The little voice was suddenly slightly uncertain. "Boy's hungry."

I weaved out of the room. I shook my husband's shoulder. "Wake up, Daddy," I muttered. "Wake up."

The little voice sang out again.

"Wake up, wake up, wake up!"

Daddy didn't stir.

It broke inside me—the sleeping, the fog, the corn, the headache, the tough day ahead.

"For heaven's sake!" I shook Daddy. "Wake up, darn you!"

The singing in the back room stopped.

There was silence for a moment, echoing my early morning tantrum.

Then the little voice came clear, sure, with a note of authority.

"Don't be a cross lady. Be a happy lady. Don't say darn. Say dear."

I said, "Dear." I tried to say it nicely—even before I'd had my coffee.

And I thought, "Me? Know it all? Know anything?"

I had been handed a lecture on living in a high young voice, a voice with only a little over two years' experience in its vocabulary.

After that, I looked at my child in the morning and saw

the happiness welling up into his face. I saw it foggily, perhaps, but I really saw it.

Watching him, I stared back down the years and remembered what it was like to wake up young.

Why, the day was a gift package. It could be filled with anything. Good. Exciting. Wondrously new.

The day was all mixed up with the blood that raced gaily through a rested small body, and the sleep that was a cushion for the hours ahead.

It was a day of golden sunshine, or a day of soft gray rain, or a day of white snow.

It didn't matter.

It was a day.

It was a thing of life offered by hands which were only sensed.

Then I grew up.

There was the expression, "Another day, another dollar."

There was the expression, "What a day."

There were others, too—all cynical, all bemoaning the beginning.

Before breakfast there were sometimes harsh words. There was the futile feeling of getting off to a wrong start, and a sour taste, and no way to fix it up. Because waking, dressing, breakfasting, getting off to work were all such racing things.

So now I lie abed one extra minute. I listen to the voice in the back room. I let the small singing, and the calling, come to me and fill me and push away the worries and the meannesses.

I get up in rhythm with the singing.

I look the sleep-rosy face right in its shining eyes.

I take its curved bright smile and I put the echo of it on my own lips.

I say, "Good morning, dear. How are you this lovely day?"
Do you know what he says?
He says, "Happy boy. Happy Mommy."
Well, maybe not always the latter. But I'm trying.
I'm following his example.
I'm trying to learn, consciously, the joy that is his without thought.

May I tell you something now?
Those words, that little anecdote, were written on my first typewriter. They were written, early in the morning, in the back bedroom of an old house in Pennsylvania, before the coffee was made.
I found them a while ago, in the bottom of a trunk.
There have been many typewriters since then, and many, many words since those faded ones on the rumpled yellow copy paper.
There have been ten years of living since then.
The little singing voice hasn't come to me in a long time. It's stronger now, and rougher, more male. The voice of a boy past twelve.
I'm glad I found the words. I'm glad I put them down.
Somehow, reading them over, I found not only the boy's lost years and an incident I had forgotten. I also found my own, as I had that morning when I was so clearly reproached.
Consider this.
Consider what our child can remind us of.
Just as the first ten years of our child's life—of our life for that matter—are blocked by more recent memories, so are the next ten years of his life—and of ours—blocked by the great good gift of the Lord.
The ignorance of what tomorrow holds!

It has been said in many ways before. But, it is very easy to forget.

Live today. This moment. This hour.

Live, but not with that wild huzzah for intemperance, "Eat, drink and be merry, for tomorrow we die." Not in desperation.

Not that way at all.

But as a child lives, totally in joy, totally in sorrow, forgetting yesterday—with tomorrow a million miles away, with today stretching infinitely to a time when anything can happen.

When we remember our child's lost years, when we save snapshots for him, or scraps of school writing, or crayoned and crooked drawings, or cute sayings, we can hold again our own lost time.

And we can use and profit by it.

When I found those long-ago written phrases, I was weary for a stretched, frightening moment.

I was weary with the knowledge of what the past ten years could have been, the glory, if only I had been wise enough to practice what I had preached on those pages.

There was another piece of paper in the old trunk, more frayed than the rest, written a longer time ago. It said:

I watch my baby. He is six months old, round as a milkweed puff and as soft.

He sits on a blanket on the floor by the davenport. He stretches small clutching hands for a hold on the tight material.

He pulls his apple rear upward. He stands.

For a triumphant, uncertain moment, he stands!

Then he drops back, knees like rubber, with a thud.

Bewilderment shadows his face. He pushes the shadow back with the curve of his smile, the firming of his chin.

He reaches small clutching hands for a hold.

He pulls upward.

I watch my child learn to roll over, to sit up, to stand—at last to walk.

I think of the cake that failed—the recipe untried again.

I think of the neighbor who snubbed a first friendly overture—and is snubbed first forever after.

I think of the knitting, the wool all tangled—project dropped.

I think of more important things begun, worked at—given up.

Perhaps I have stopped trying to pull my mind up from a squatting position. Perhaps it's been a long time since I have made my mind stand straight and proud and walk ahead with a new thought.

Looks. Faith. Friends. Church. Husband. Reading. Dreams. Devotion. Cooking. Housework.

Which ones are failing for lack of trying?

Adult wisdom is all right, I think, in its place. But as the years run along, adults tend to let slip from their lax fingers many successes, many joys that might have been theirs if they had just clutched one more time—pulled upward one more time.

I watch my baby.

"So much to learn," I think with that adult wisdom. "Poor darling. So much to learn."

I yearn a little.

But I know, just the same, that he will be all right.

He will learn to stand without hanging on.

Because it never occurs to him not to try again, over and over, until what was hard becomes easy.

There is a drive in him, a force. There is a compulsion that insures his ultimate victory.

The same force is in me, no matter what my age. It is hidden under the known disappointments, the laziness that is a part of us all.

But it's there—flabby, unused, but waiting.

I watch my baby.

The first thing I know, he'll be walking all by himself.

And so can I, if I keep at it and try even half as hard as he does.

When I read those words, ten years later, I felt a little better. In this department of stubbornness and repetitive trying, I have, with great effort, managed to take my own advice.

The third piece of yellow copy paper told a third forgotten story.

It is the middle of the night.

The quiet house holds sleep as tenderly as a tangible.

Suddenly the sleep, the quiet, the tenderness are split wide open.

They are torn with the screams of my dreaming child.

My feet hit the floor. Gown and hair fly as I race to the boy's room. My warm arms are quick to lift and hold and cherish. My voice is reassurance.

I make of myself a cradle of security for the trembling body, the troubled small mind.

So I rock, holding the quiet once more around both of us.

I look down at the crescent lashes against the young cheeks.
I think about fear, my child's fear.

The dark is unknown, I think. In the dreaming time all the
daylight terrors are loosed.

I wish I might always be here, be strong enough, be right
enough, to put the fear to rest.

There is a foolishness in my child's terror. The room in
which he sleeps blackly is peopled with the same furniture,
the same windows, the same curtains, the same bed, as it is in
the sunlight.

Rocking, thinking, I know that as it is with my child's
room, so it is with the rooms of my own life.

The furniture of my life is in the same position in time of
panic, worry, and fear as it is when I am serene and believing.

And from the foolishness, the unabashed and unbased terror
of my child, I can draw a parallel and learn a lesson.

My child's weakness is the source of my strength. I hold
him. I reason with him. I assure him that the life I have been
privileged to give him is good, that there is nothing to fear.
As I do, I slowly add to my own vocabulary the words of
courage, the feeling of courage, with which I am trying to
endow him.

"Teach me, son," I wrote then on the slips of paper.

Teach me, son, I have said to myself many times in the days
since.

Teach me to find again my own lost years and the sweet
tang of childhood.

Teach me to hold my life and treasure it and use it—with
sureness, with instinct, with a bravery young, unweighed, and
unbalanced.

If I were writing on a piece of yellow copy paper now, in

78

the back bedroom of an old house in Pennsylvania, I would add a few more paragraphs.

I would say:

Son, within all of us there are the lost years—the time of living when to feel was exquisite, sharp, of the moment.

The day will come when you will be grown, when you will look at your life and study the symmetry or the distortion of it. You will ask yourself how it came to be as it is.

When did the base of its rhythmed grace begin? Or how did the crack start that widened to adult ugliness?

Those first ten years of breathing, during which you learned more than you will at any other time, are separated from you by the other years, the older, more conscious years, which block out that which is first and most real.

We can make no apologies for those years, son, your father and I. Not for ourselves or the others of our time. Not even for the world of our time. It is the age in which you were given your existence. We are the people, good or ill, to whom you were entrusted.

There is in us the deep desire to be all that we can to you. There are in us, also, many other depths which have nothing to do with you at all, but which will have influenced you.

We hope, your father and I, with a hope almost beyond a prayer, that we will see how it turns out, what becomes of you, born of us and the era.

Sometimes that seems like a great deal to ask.

But whether we do or not, we will never know who has been the teacher and who the student. We may have learned more than we have taught.

We have gained more than we have given.

Some of your gifts to us during your lost years, I have found and tried to set down here for your remembering.

I have told them as stories, because you loved stories when you were small and because that is easiest for me to do.

You see, from earliest beginnings, a writer absorbs atmosphere, feeling, color. At the typewriter, or with a pencil in hand, with eyes closed, thoughts stirred and jumbled, a writer can be removed backward to twenty, to sixteen, to twelve.

And sometimes even to ten and before.

If you are a writer and a mother, you can do this quite easily.

It should, I suppose, make me a better writer. It should, I pray, make me a better mother.

But whether it does or not, the stories, no matter what their form, are true. And I thank you for them, son.

CHAPTER ☆ *2* ☆

☆

☆

HERE'S YOUR LUCK, GRANDPA

☆

Each day started the same way.

Each morning, just about the time Eddie started to pull up his second sock, there came a thump-thumpety-thump-thump on the door of the small house.

He tried to fool the knock. Today he would be very slow and the knock would come before the socks. Or this morning he would hurry and be all dressed when the knock came.

But hurry or dawdle, the knock always came just when he began to pull up that second sock, sometimes three toes in, but always the second sock.

He didn't run from where he was, even knowing it was coming. He sat still, on the floor, on the bed, with his hands hanging over the sock, to hear the door open.

"Anybody home?" Grandpa would cry.

It was like the knock, always the same.

Eddie listened for the answer.

"How are you, Dad?" Mother usually asked.

Eddie would sit there making his mouth move with Grandpa's words.

"Can't complain," the whisper and Grandpa would say together. "Can't complain at all."

Then, as if something had been settled, or proven safe, he would yank at the sock, reach for the shoe that matched, tie a quick loose knot, get up and walk into the living room.

Grandpa always sat in the big chair, with the paper he brought for Mother to read after they were gone.

The next thing he would say, looking over the paper and his glasses, was, "How's my boy?"

Eddie didn't have to answer that at all. It didn't matter. He had looked at Grandpa and Grandpa had looked at him, and it was all right.

He knew Grandpa. Sometimes with Mother, Eddie was a "naughty little boy." Sometimes with Daddy, he was a "don't bother me."

But with Grandpa he was a grandson.

It was in Grandpa's eyes and the way he put his hand, always shaking and never heavy, on Eddie's head for just a second when he was walking by. "This is my grandson," Grandpa would say to anybody who stopped long enough to hear it. "This is my grandson." Look the other way, kick your feet, make a face, it still felt warm. "This is my grandson."

Next after the knock, the saying, the seeing, Eddie put on his coat and walked out the door with Grandpa. He waved to Mother. The old car started somehow and the two small plastic cars tied under the rear view mirror would jump and swing.

"I gave you those little cars," Eddie said, almost every morning.

"That you did," Grandpa would say, as if it had never been mentioned before. "Couldn't go anywhere without them."

Eddie sat back then, as if something had again been settled, and watched the way to kindergarten through the soiled car window. Everything looked better through a window that wasn't too shining.

Just before he got to the kindergarten room, Grandpa stopped. He looked down. He leaned his face close. Eddie could see his beard. It was white, not dark like Daddy's. Maybe the whiteness was what made it not rough.

Close that way, Grandpa's eyes looked very big and brown. The whole world seemed to swim in velvet.

He knew what Grandpa wanted and he was ready with it. Eddie was five and a half. Maybe he should worry about other kids. But you can't worry about what doesn't come into your mind. All that was in Eddie's mind—with Grandpa so close he could see his head shake, bent over like that—was the asking in Grandpa's eyes.

So he leaned toward him and put his lips on Grandpa's cheek and leaned back and crossed his middle finger over his first finger and said, "Here's your luck, Grandpa."

For a very little time they smiled at each other. Then Grandpa straightened up and touched Eddie on the head. He seemed to look younger for a moment.

After that, the day began—for both of them.

Just before noon, when Eddie came out, the old car was in front of the school. Grandpa was in it and he didn't pretend to be thinking of something else, like fixing his radios. He looked straight out, waiting for his grandson. Eddie would shuffle along to make it last, then climb in slowly and not look at Grandpa, but just sit.

It always came. "How did it go, boy?" Grandpa asked next. "I hate school," Eddie would cry.

Mother got excited when he said that. But not Grandpa. He just grinned and held the flap of his pocket out, and there it was—the reward for sticking out the morning. The little brown bag with penny things in it, that showed Grandpa knew about school.

No thank you's for Grandpa. He knew how the bag felt when Eddie's fingers touched the edge of it. The funny little moment when you don't know what is in it and want to know, but have to keep from hurrying so that wanting to know can last an extra minute.

Eddie took a candy and gave Grandpa one. Then he ate all the rest. Just before lunch.

If anybody ever said anything, like Mother or Daddy or even Grandma, Grandpa always snorted. "Whose grandson is he, for pity's sake? I'll take care of my own grandson."

That's the way the days were. Every day.

There was a time before kindergarten, too. But time ran together. A man with brown eyes and white hair leaned over Eddie and solemnly offered his necktie to pull on. The man let Eddie put on his big hat and it flopped way down over his face. The man held Eddie before he went to sleep sometimes, and he had shaky arms that were almost like a teeter-babe, and he sang in a voice that was shaky, too.

But those other things were long ago, when Eddie was small and couldn't dress himself. They ran into each other more and more and grew further and further away, and someday they would be gone.

Then, there came the day that wasn't like any other day.

84

Eddie woke up and the house was quiet. He thought he'd get dressed fast and really fool the knock. He started in a flurry.

But while he was looking for a shirt, he found a piece of chalk back in a corner of the drawer. He went into the closet to look for the blackboard. There was an old cooky in a bag. He sat down and ate it. There was a comic book. He pulled it out.

He was through with the chalk, the cooky, the comic book. Nobody had called him. The day didn't have an early feeling. There was an already-in-kindergarten sun.

Eddie stood for a moment in the middle of the room, a strangeness all through him as though he could smell that this day was different.

The door opened.

Mother came in softly and closed the door. She put out her arms. Eddie went to stand in their circle. He looked up at her.

"I have to tell you something, son," she said. Soft. Uncross. No sigh. No brightness.

He watched her swallow. The smell of differentness was very sharp now.

"Last night," Mother went on, "in the middle of the night, without anything hurting at all, Grandpa went on his long night-night."

Flashing thoughts hit against each other.

Night-night, until Eddie turned four, was good night.

Long night-night was that trip up and up, where you couldn't hold anybody's hand and had to go alone and you couldn't take any toys—up and up to that place that was all shining and God was there and everybody was happy.

He felt the smile tickle the corners of his mouth. The smile for feeling wonderful. For walking into the Christmas morn-

ing room. Or riding little cars at Playland, red and green and
yellow.

"Mom," he said through the smile, feeling it grow, "Oh,
Mom, I bet he'll have fun up there."

He looked quickly at his mother's eyes to see if they were
clear and proud. She liked the special smile, always. Her eyes
were dark, like Grandpa's, only without any light in them
at all.

She nodded. "My darling," she said softly. "Oh, my darling!"

Eddie couldn't tell whether she was talking about him or
about Grandpa.

He found himself putting one hand over hers. He leaned
forward, close to her. He heard Grandpa's voice very clearly.

He said the words he heard, the way he always whispered
"Can't complain" while Grandpa said it in the other room.

He said, "Be glad it wasn't me."

Mother jumped back. Her hands jumped on his shoulders.

"It's the first thing Dad would have———." She stopped.

Eddie ducked out from under her hands. Grandpa *had* said
it. Anybody knew that.

Mother stood up quickly. "Today will be different, dear,"
she said. "You'll stay home and Daddy is home. Aunt Jean
and Uncle Steve are here and—and Grandma is in Mother's
bed. You must be very quiet."

There was no knock with the second sock, even though he
dressed very slowly.

Grandma made a big warm hump on the bed. She had her
bathrobe on, as if even the blankets didn't keep her snug
enough.

Eddie made a running jump and landed on the bed beside
her.

"Boo, Martha Finnegan," he cried.

The yell seemed to have echoes. He slid very carefully, shoes and all, down under the blankets beside Grandma, and pushed himself against her.

Her whole big body was shivering. He reached for her arm and pulled it away from her face. There were no tears in her eyes nor any redness around them.

"Did you know Grandpa went on his long night-night?" Eddie felt full of news and important. "Did Mother tell you?"

Grandma swallowed twice. "Yes, dear." She swallowed again. "I know."

He leaned up on one elbow and studied her face. "You don't look very happy about it," he said at last.

Grandma's face turned into a rubber finger puppet, the kind you can squeeze all ways. He felt her breath pull up slowly.

"I am happy for Grandpa," she said, as slow as her breath. "He was old and very tired and he wouldn't rest and God made him rest."

That's the way it is, he thought. Grandpa always hurries up all the stairs and runs down them.

"Are you going to cry?" he asked Grandma.

She shook her head.

"You've got *me*," he said.

She nodded slowly.

He laughed. "Grandpa is a cute old man." Mother sometimes said that to Daddy.

"Go now," Grandma said.

He climbed out right away and walked across the room, feeling not loved, and with that smell of something strange in his nose. Grandma made a funny noise just as he got to the door. He ran, sliding on the floor, quickly to the kitchen.

87

The kitchen was full of people. They all walked with a shuffle and a whispering. It stopped him.

There really weren't so many when he looked around. Just Aunt and Uncle, and the friendly neighbor who was Gary's mother. Daddy was there, too. He sat at the desk with the telephone to his ear.

"That's right," he said. "New York City. The message is, Dad died last night. Heart. Funeral Monday at three. Signed, Dave."

"Have some juice," Aunt Jean offered.

Uncle Steve reached in his pocket and brought out a stick of gum. "For after breakfast."

Eddie stared at it steadily and tried not to look at the pocket. All he could see was a brown paper bag, and sometimes it had gum as well as candy.

"I don't want any juice," he said. "I don't want any breakfast. I hate gum."

He started for the bedroom. He stopped beside Daddy. *Died last night. Died last night.*

"Will there be company?" he asked.

Daddy shook his head. "It's too far. But they'll send flowers. That will be nice, won't it?"

He thought about it. On your long night-night you didn't need flowers, or toys, or anything or anybody. You were just happy.

But how could Grandpa sit still and just be happy? He had to work.

"Work's the ticket, boy." Grandpa said that.

"Work's the answer," he said.

Eddie said, "I bet Grandpa's awful busy up there in Heaven."

Daddy smiled a little. "Doing what?"

88

He knew right away. "Sweeping off the stars for God."

Behind him Mother's breath caught sharply.

His father's eyes were suddenly full. The tears sprang out. Mother hadn't cried. Grandma hadn't. But Daddy was crying. A man. It made Eddie's heart pound.

He pulled himself roughly away from his father. He ran across the room, yanked open the door and raced through, not shutting it behind him. He scurried across the alley and pushed open the gate to Gary's back yard.

He ran to Gary's house and yelled, "Gary, Gary, come out and play."

Gary came right away.

He and Gary were rough and yelling and played guns. All day bang-bang guns. With time out for a sandwich the neighbor lady gave them.

Bang-bang!

Shoot 'em dead!

Dead.

When it began to get dark, his father came through the gate and took his hand and led him home. Mother gave him supper. Daddy put him to bed.

Daddy sat at the side of the bed for a long time, scratching Eddie's back gently and humming. Then he turned off the lights and went out.

Eddie lay there. He thought about Gary's guns. He thought about the circus. He thought, suddenly and without warning and with a desperate need, of his old teddy bear.

He got out of bed and turned on the light. He opened the closet door and rummaged around. At last he found the teddy bear. One ear was off and sticky jam rimmed his fat front. He hadn't been taken to bed for a long time.

"Poor Teddy," Eddie said softly. "Poor Teddy."

There were voices in the living room now.

Eddie called to his father. He came right away.

"What are you doing out there? Who's rumbling?" Eddie asked.

It was quiet for a minute.

Then his father said, "The minister is here."

"Why?"

It was quiet for another little time.

"When somebody is dead, son, you have to make arrangements for a funeral. Come on now, I'll tuck you in again."

Somebody is dead.

His father smoothed the pillow, and fastened the sheet smooth the way Eddie liked it, and turned off the light again.

"Go to sleep now," he ordered.

"I've got a right to be out there," Eddie found himself saying. "I'm part of this family."

His father's voice sounded muffled. "A big part," he said. "More than you know."

He leaned over and kissed Eddie full on the mouth. That had never happened before.

Eddie heard the door shut. He felt the darkness seep all around him.

He clutched the teddy bear and put his face down into it.

It wasn't his darkness. It wasn't like it always had been. It was blacker and full of a breathing.

The breathing made the word Daddy had said on the phone.

Died.

It made the word Daddy had said in the living room.

Dead.

Dead. Not long night-night. Dead.

90

He sat up and stared into what he could not see. He slammed the teddy bear away from him.

He said, aloud, through the hard feeling in his throat and the hammering in his heart, "Grandpa is dead. Grandpa is dead. Grandpa is dead."

He began to sob.

He was so afraid he couldn't even yell for anybody.

The darkness was all full of the words now. It was reaching to grab him. He tried frantically to see Grandpa's eyes through it. He couldn't remember them. He couldn't remember anything about Grandpa.

Died. Dead.

It came quickly, almost sharply. It wasn't a loud sound, but it rode right through all the sobs and the fear.

It said, in Eddie's ear, usual and sure and clean, "This is my grandson. I'll take care of my own grandson."

It was as good as a pair of arms, as good as the brown bag of candy.

Eddie lay back and scrubbed at his eyes. He listened to the voice. It drowned out the new words.

"Anybody home?"

Eddie nodded. "How are you, Grandpa?" He thought it. He didn't say it.

"Can't complain," the voice said comfortably. "Can't complain at all. How's my boy?"

Eddie didn't have to answer that. It didn't matter, just like any morning.

"This is my grandson." It was as if Grandpa were making one of those proud introductions.

It didn't matter that Eddie couldn't see Grandpa any more. Grandpa wasn't a seeing anyhow. He was a way to feel.

The whole room was full of the feel of Grandpa.

91

Soft. Kind. There.

Eddie sat up again and reached around until he found the teddy bear. He lay down and tucked it against his cheek. He let the darkness grow warm and good again.

Grandpa would have fun up in Heaven, all right. He probably most likely really *was* sweeping off the stars for God.

But he was here, too—which was a wonderful thing, but not to be surprised at.

There was something bothering Eddie still, even with the grown-up nasty words gone, even with Grandpa here. Something forgotten.

Then he remembered it.

He put his lips against the teddy bear's fur. It felt soft like a white beard. He crossed his middle finger over his first finger.

"Here's your luck, Grandpa," he whispered.

Then he rolled over and dropped right into sleep.

CHAPTER ☆ *3* ☆

HEARTBREAK NUMBER ONE

☆

In the mornings, that summer when he was nine, stretching out in bed, with the hot sun slamming behind the curtains and breathing on the top of his head, Joe felt the length of himself reaching farther than it ever had before.

Sometimes he would roll over and all his muscles would feel silky in his skin and he'd laugh out loud. Or begin to sing at the top of his lungs. Songs about pirates.

The summer Joe was nine his father stopped being a traveling salesman. They had a stay-put house for the first time he could remember. His father bought a small hardware store in Booneville. The house was white, with a big yard.

It seemed to seep into the three of them.

Joe's mother hung up the washing as if she planned to use those same lines in the sunny part of the yard until she was too old to reach up.

His father planted bushes by the front fence, as if he intended to prune them a hundred years later.

Joe rode his bike past the school and got the feeling of how it would be to walk out of there with a diploma.

He wasn't lonely, although he was an only child and he didn't know any of the boys in the block or in the town. He had a bicycle for the first time in his life. He had the puppet theater he had made. He had books and the models he worked endlessly. He was never lonely.

But he did look around. He did wait.

One day he rode past the schoolhouse and there were two boys. All over each other, they were, grunting, scratching, pounding. They raised a dust from the dirty pavement. They raised another kind of dust, too—the fierce, deep, shocking hate that two small boys, suddenly goaded against each other, can generate.

Joe got off his bike and watched them. The smaller one was getting the worst of it. A trickle of blood mixed with the dirt on his cheek. One eye was swollen.

Joe found himself yelling, "Hey, leave him alone. You hurt him enough."

The bigger boy never swung his head. "Nuts to you," he yelled back.

The smaller boy didn't even seem to know Joe was there. He just kept slogging, trying to get his fist free, trying to find room to pull it back, succeeding at neither.

Suddenly Joe was in the middle of it, he the new kid, the only child, the one who'd never taken a blow nor given one. He had the bigger boy by the shirt. He heard it rip, felt it give.

He had him by the neck, his skin slippery and hot against his palms. He pulled on him. The feeling of the morning

strength was all through him. The boy came—partly because
Joe pulled, partly because he wanted to turn, as he did,
and slug Joe.

Joe sat down.

He got up again, quickly.

They stood there, toe to toe, the bigger boy and Joe. When
he hit Joe it hurt, sharp, stinging, as if his skin had cracked.
But Joe managed to hit him back.

After a while they both stopped, as if they'd talked it over
and decided it was the sensible thing to do. They stood facing
each other, drawing great deep breaths.

Then, simultaneously, they swung to look at the smaller
boy.

He was lying on the grass and his face was very white where
it wasn't very dirty. He looked up at them with the bluest
eyes Joe had ever seen. Joe went over to him and knelt down.

"You hurt?" he asked.

The boy shook his head. The little streak of blood had
dried on his cheek.

"He's not hurt," the bigger boy cried. "Dirty sneak."

He turned and limped away.

Joe sat down beside the boy. He brushed off his jeans and
touched his stomach gingerly.

"That kid's got a punch," he said, as if he'd tried all kinds
and gave credit where it was due. "What's his name?"

"Toby." The boy sat up. "So have you got a punch." He
was smaller even than Joe had thought, and thinner too. "My
name's Steve."

"I'm Joe," Joe said. He reached across the curb and picked
up his gun. He twirled it around his finger.

He felt fine.

It was like D'Artagnan, jumping down out of a tree with

his sword ready, just when the going got tough for the other
Musketeers.

It was the captain of the ship, loosening his bonds just in
time to grab the upraised hand of the pirate about to stab his
first mate.

It was big shot and protective and he liked it. You don't
have many chances to feel that way when you're nine.

Steve stood up. Joe did, too. He towered over Steve and
it made the feeling even better.

"Lemme see your gun," Steve commanded.

Joe gave it to him.

Steve clicked it, held it low to his hip, and turned quickly,
with a swing that was like a snake. The gun pointed at Joe
and spoke sharply. Twice.

Joe died right and proper.

He put the look of surprise on his face and let his mouth
sag. He reached slowly, painfully, with both hands, for the
pit of his stomach. He clawed at it a moment, then slipped
sideways, straight at first, followed by a limpness that threw
his arms out above his head on the ground.

He lay still, eyes closed, agony in his mind so that it would
stay on his face.

Steve spoke finally, in a hushed voice.

"Keen," he whispered. "Keen. Boy, you sure can croak."

The first flicker of a wonderful and good feeling began that
very moment—when Joe was on the ground and a pebble bit
into his shoulder and he kept his eyes closed.

In his mind was the picture of Steve, whom he'd saved. In
his ears was the sound of Steve's admiration. He held them
both as long as he could.

Then he opened his eyes and jumped up. He reached out a
hand for the gun. Steve gave it to him.

Joe said, "I collect knights." He didn't look up.

Steve laughed. "What kind? Starry? Rainy?"

Joe laughed, too. This time he looked up. "Never mind," he said.

Nobody knew about the knights, or the foils, or the pretend games.

Steve said, "Hey, where you got those knights?"

"At home. In my room."

"Well, let's go," he prodded. "Only we better go down to Rand's Creek and wash off this mess, or we'll catch it when we get there."

Joe got on the bike and Steve jumped on the handlebars as if it were all settled. He showed Joe the way to the creek. Joe hadn't been there, and as far as he knew he wasn't allowed.

It was some place, all right—down a stiff hill and hidden, and deep enough so that they could wade in to their shoulders and swim around a little. Steve didn't swim. Joe showed off. His mother saw to it that he had swimming lessons.

After a little they lay on a flat piece of ground where the sun splattered through the trees and turned them shady and golden.

Joe never was so happy in his life.

That began the summer when Joe was nine. In the morning when he was awake but with his eyes still closed, still holding the night against his lids, the feeling came.

It fooled him at first, because it was like Christmas. Then he would remember it was summer and that the feeling wasn't a matter of season or getting things. It was a matter of Steve.

Steve would be up and waiting, three blocks over and two blocks down. Or he would be outside, swinging on the gate, watching for Joe's curtains to go up. Wherever he was, their

97

plans were already laid, made in the purple dusk of the night before.

Sometimes they were Huckleberry Finn and Tom Sawyer. Those times they packed sandwiches and went without shoes and took the long way over the hill to the creek. For one whole week they hammered and nailed in the old shed behind the house, and came out with a barrel-stave raft, which they portaged to the creek and sat on, regally, although there wasn't enough current to take them anywhere.

Sometimes they were pirates. They rifled an old trunk they found in the attic. They went down to the Thrift Shop and Joe spent the money he'd been saving for a model ship. They bought old clothes and tricked themselves out in costumes worthy of Captain Hook. They took turns being Smee.

Steve was good about taking turns. Joe got a little piggish sometimes, wanting to be head man. But Steve would smile a sudden strange sweet smile and shake his head, and Joe would feel foolish and give in.

They made puppets. They went to the Saturday movies and bought hot dogs afterward. They drew pictures of swordsmen and knights on rainy afternoons in Joe's kitchen.

They shared a hundred worlds. Joe put himself to sleep each night planning the world for tomorrow—for Steve and himself.

Steve and himself.

He supposed there were other boys on the street, at the creek, in the movies, that summer. He must have heard them and maybe talked to them once in a while. But he didn't play with them. He and Steve didn't let any of them into any of their worlds.

"Those jerks," Steve would say scornfully. "All they want

is fighting and football and yelling around. What do they know about King Arthur?"

Steve knew about King Arthur. He knew about a lot of other things Joe hadn't found out yet, that summer when he was nine. Because, amazing as it was, Steve was eleven close to twelve—little and thin and white, but close to twelve.

One time Joe's mother said, "I think I'll just walk along with you this morning and call on Steve's mother. You boys are such great friends, it's only polite to get acquainted."

Joe didn't know why, but he didn't want her to.

In all of their traveling he'd never seen anything like Steve's tumbledown house with weeds growing all around it. He'd never seen anything like Steve's mother, with babies of all sizes seeming to grow around her, quick with a slap and a yell, but tolerating him as if one more couldn't possibly matter. Or Steve's father, always in his undershirt and smelling funny and howling, "Can't a man get a little rest, for gawsakes?"

But he didn't know how to say it.

So he walked beside his own neat mother with her only child who had a big sunny room to himself and more toys than he knew what to do with. He prayed nothing would happen, like her deciding Steve wasn't good enough for her precious son.

Nothing did happen. Steve's mother sat with Joe's on the creaking swing on the slanting porch.

"Let's just skunch down here and listen in," Steve suggested.

They skunched in the weeds.

Steve's mother said, in her tired voice, "Them boys are sure set on each other. Steve ain't had many treats like you folks give him."

"It's nothing, nothing," Joe's mother said quickly, embarrassed, Joe could tell.

He listened to her and it was the first time his mother had come into focus since the day he met Steve, the day he had a best friend.

He thought of the lunches she'd packed for them.

He thought of the time she and his father took them into the city to the circus, and once to the beach.

He thought of how she'd gotten into the habit of buying two of everything whenever she went shopping and brought home presents.

He thought of the way she patted Steve's head sometimes, as if she loved him too, almost as if she were grateful to him.

Steve's mother talked next. "I hope," she said thinly, "your boy never gets too fancy for Steve. It'd bust Steve wide open."

Joe looked toward Steve, skunched there in the weeds. Blood brothers, friends until death, he thought. He grinned at Steve. Steve smiled back, but it wasn't full. He didn't look Joe quite in the eye.

His mother said, "I'm glad they're friends, too——"

Steve whispered sharply, "Let's get away from this mush."

They went.

And it was August without their knowing it.

His mother fixed picnics in the big hamper she'd swiped from his father's store. And once, on a weekend, his folks drove more than a hundred miles to a place where there was a big aquarium, and they rented two rooms. Steve and Joe had one all to themselves, as if they were grown-up, roommates in college.

There were other times, too. They'd saunter down Main Street together, looking in the windows, and pretend to buy whatever they wanted. The day they coaxed a can of paint out of Joe's father and painted the whole inside of the shack, first cutting out two crooked windows, and got old furniture and put it there and fixed a sign over the door.

PIRATE'S DEN, it warned. KEEP OUT!!!

The days stretched, as Joe used to stretch on the bed. The boys felt strong and ready for any adventure. They tied themselves together with star-hung nights of sleep. There was more to do than even their great sleepy timeless hours allowed.

And when they had done everything they could think of, they'd start all over again.

Joe loved the pattern. From puppets to models to knights to pirates. To Tom Sawyer, to King Arthur, to searching for secret gold by the creek. He was nine and he never tired of it.

Suddenly, with a shock like thunder rolling from a clear sky and lightning stabbing from fluffy clouds, it was over. The Labor Day parade was over. The flag was run up atop the school.

The summer was gone.

The new clothes were laid out and Joe put them on slowly. His hands shook. His mouth was so dry he couldn't eat any breakfast, only drink the milk.

It had never been easy at school. Practically always, it seemed, his father had to move in the middle of the year, after the beginning.

He never got used to walking into a working classroom with a smiling principal. He always minded the way everything stopped and all the eyes switched to him, blue, brown and gray, unfriendly or waiting to see.

Above all, he never got used to the playground at recess. You couldn't stagger and fall there. You couldn't tell anybody about the knights, or the costumes, or pretending, or pirates. Not on the playground, you couldn't.

Everybody played touchball and knew the rules. The teacher always pushed Joe in the middle of it, he being such a big boy for his age.

But somehow, the kids managed to push him out again when they chose up sides. That left Joe with the thin boys, the sickly ones, the slow thinkers.

So he went off by himself, on the edge of all the noise, and hit a fencing stance and ran the robbers through. Pretty soon the bell rang.

Remembering all this while he dressed and drank his milk, put the shakes in his hands and the dryness in his mouth.

Then he thought of Steve, and it was all right.

This time it was different. This was a school for always, like the house and his father's store. Steve was a friend for always, and they'd walk to school together. Joe would never be alone on the playground again. Steve knew his way around. Steve would show him.

Joe kissed his mother and let her smooth his hair. Then he got on his bike and pedaled fast to Steve's house.

The ranks of children had thinned in the weedy yard, pruned by the first day of school. Joe banked the bike and went up to the porch steps.

"Steve," he called, "let's go."

He stared around, looking it all over, feeling good about it—the easy way the house leaned, the familiar little kids on the porch and the sound of the radio blaring inside. He couldn't yell for Steve above the noise, he realized. He went to the screen door.

One of the little ones yelled, "Steve, he's here."

She grinned. She had the echo of Steve's sweet smile. Joe grinned back.

It was a fine morning, hot already, and his mother had put lemonade in his new lunch box.

From somewhere inside the house he heard Steve's voice. "Tell him to go along. I'm not ready."

Joe stood up straight, a funny feeling tickling his back, just thinking of walking in the school alone.

The little one smiled again. "He's not ready," she repeated, pushing her nose against the screen.

"I'll wait," he said.

"He'll wait," she parroted, switching her head around.

Steve's voice sounded faraway, as if he were fading. "I said tell him to get going."

Joe wanted to walk away, across the sagging porch and down the steps and on his bike and away. But he was nine years old. He couldn't.

He yelled, "Hey, Steve, I'll wait."

Somebody turned the radio down.

Steve's father cried, "Can't a man sleep, for gawsakes?"

Joe stood rooted to the spot. He could hear Steve's mother's voice. He could hear the sizzing sort of sound of Steve's whisper, through the other outdoor noises.

He heard feet coming and the tickling feeling in his spine began to go away. But it was Steve's mother who came to the other side of the screen.

"You run along, kid."

"We'll be late," he insisted, not thinking, just hearing the words come out of her mouth. "We shouldn't be late the first day."

She smoothed back her hair and tightened her mouth a little. "Well," she snapped, "then you run along."

"But I don't want——"

Her face was suddenly annoyed. "Look," she said sharply,

"I got things to do besides argue. Steve and Toby, they always go to school together. They're fifth grade. Toby's most likely wondering why Steve ain't stopped by." Her voice softened. "You run along."

Joe turned on his heel and walked away. He pushed his bike, suddenly too tired to get up on it.

He went to school. It was all a blur, a waiting blur until recess. He stood on the edge of the playground and watched the touchball.

Steve and Toby were in the middle of it, running and laughing. Steve didn't look Joe's way—not once.

After school, Joe went to Rand's Creek and lay at its edge, just pulling the long thin grasses. He waited for Steve to come. For a long time he expected him. Then he got on his bicycle and raced it, hard, all the way home. Maybe Steve was waiting for him on the gate.

He wasn't.

Every morning Joe got up with a strange feeling. He got dressed, slowly, so as to give Steve plenty of time to stop by his house. He ate as little breakfast as his mother would allow, and he walked slowly to school, not taking the bike because maybe Steve would catch up with him.

He did what he was told and waited for recess. But the touchball always made a circle around Steve that he couldn't break.

Every day after school, for a week or maybe more, he went to Steve's house. Steve never came to the door. Once Joe saw him plainly inside. Another time, he watched him run across the back field with Toby when he saw Joe coming.

He spent most of the afternoons at Rand's Creek after his check-up. He tried to figure out what he'd done wrong.

He had a strange feeling of guilt inside him, as if he'd done

one of the things his father told him boys don't do, or as if he'd used the words you weren't supposed to say.

But he couldn't think of anything. He tried, very hard, but he couldn't think of a thing.

It was worst of all going to bed. There wasn't anything to plan on, falling asleep, except maybe tomorrow Steve would come and be with him and it would be the way it had been.

But the days moved on, the slow heavy school days, the endless Saturdays, and Steve didn't come.

Then, one day, when Joe walked up the path, there he was. Not running into the house. There. He stood with his hands on his belt, and he looked skinny and white and blue-eyed—and tough.

"Get off my property," he said loudly. "Quit bothering me. Quit following me around. Get off my property, baby, and don't come back."

"You skunk," Joe yelled, not meaning to, just finding the words all there, bottled up from the times he'd come and been pushed away. "You dirty sneak. Who you think you are, anyway? The King of Siam?"

Tears were in his eyes and on his cheeks. He hated them, but, like the words, he couldn't do a thing about them. He just cried and yelled—everything he'd ever heard or been told not to say.

Steve stood, quiet enough, his fists and head cocked. When Joe had yelled it all, he moved toward him slowly.

"I got a right," he said, and it sounded soft and grown-up after all Joe's noise, "to be friends with anybody I want to. See? If Toby and me hadn't had that fight, you think I'd ever of played with you?"

He was close to Joe now and his fists were lifting. "I'm sick of you," he shouted suddenly. "I'm tired of the same old

booby pretend games. Sick and tired of you and your kinder-
garten-baby play."

His eyes were pale blue. Joe couldn't see his friend anywhere on his face. The lump in his throat weighed a ton.

"You wanna make something of it?" Steve asked, almost
casually.

Joe took a deep breath and stared at him. He could lick
him all right—as Toby had—if he put his heart into it.

Only his heart wasn't in it.

He shook his head. He turned away.

"Dirty sneak," he called over his shoulder.

"Yellow-belly baby, baby, baby. Spoiled-cat crybaby," Steve
yelled at him. His voice sounded thick and funny.

Joe crawled home, his tail between his legs. He was an
only, truly an only, for the first time in his life. Alone and
lost and desperate.

He went in the back way and up to his room and threw
himself on the bed and howled. He didn't care if his mother
heard, or the neighbors, or the whole town. Let them think
he'd broken a leg. Nothing could shut him up.

Passing time shut him up, of course. When he was quieter
he knew that his mother sat on the bed beside him, rubbing
his back in a way she had.

"I didn't do anything, Mom," he said. "What did I do?" he
asked. "I hate him, hate him, hate him," he yelled.

She just shook her head, slowly, and there were tears running down her cheeks. "I loved him, too, son," she said. "Poor
little skinny guy, so sweet and gentle."

"Nuts," Joe cried. "Nuts to him. Dirty sneak."

He lay there, dimly remembering Toby's same phrase,
wondering why Toby said it, and if it was for the same reason.

His mother began to talk through the funny quiet gasp of his breathing.

"It worried us, son, your father and me. Always together, and you never having a close friend before, and thinking the sun rose and set in him. But you were so happy——." She stopped. She took his face in both her hands and forced him to look at her. "Never," she said seriously, as if she were talking to another grownup, "never give your entire self to another person. Save a little, to make your own self happy if he——if he——." She began to cry.

She cried hard enough that it frightened Joe and he stopped.

That night his father took him for a long walk. They didn't say much of anything. Joe wasn't even very much aware of his father beside him.

They were all the way back home before his father said, out of a clear sky, "He'll come back, lad. He'll come back. That kind always do, I promise you."

Just before they went into the house he added, "You stay away from there, hear? It doesn't pay to humble yourself."

Inside the door he swung Joe around and rubbed his hair roughly. "When he comes back," he said very softly, "don't expect it to be the same. It will never be the same."

The next night when Joe came home from going to the grocery, his father was there and on his mother's lap was a cocker spaniel puppy. It was the color of coffee with cream in it. It was an awfully nice puppy and took to Joe right away.

But it wasn't Steve.

Joe was kept busy training him, though.

They did a lot of things together the rest of that year, his folks and Joe. He found out there were other kids on the block, too. Most of them were younger than he, but they started coming around. They liked to play pretend—Western mostly. It wasn't too different from King Arthur and pirates. It shortened the late afternoons.

But after supper, when the littler ones had been called in, Joe would get on his bicycle and ride around. Boys he knew would holler at him and he'd holler back. But he kept going. To Rand's Creek and down the Main Street and up over the hill. He found a path, or made one, where he could see Steve's house without being seen.

He'd hang one foot over his bike and watch, down below him in the twilight, while Steve and Toby threw a football. Joe didn't know how to throw a football yet.

He dreamed at night, awake or asleep. It was always summer. Always that summer.

His father was right, too.

Steve came back.

He just rode up one Saturday after Christmas and asked, "You sore?"

Joe shook his head. "I got nothing against you," he said.

It was what his father had told him to say if this happened.

Anyhow, he was ten by then.

"Good," Steve smiled. "Long as you're sorry you dropped me, let's play."

Joe started to open his mouth. He shut it again. "Sure," he agreed. "Sure. Where's Toby?"

Steve snorted. "Toby—that jerk. All he thinks about is football. I'm tired of football. Let's get out those knights."

They did.

Joe's father was right again, though. It wasn't the same.

The other kids still came around—the smaller ones on the street, the ones who waved to Joe, the ones from school.

They were there, and Steve didn't like it. Anyhow, he

looked different to Joe, Steve did. It wasn't the same and it didn't last long.

But Joe didn't care—not in the least.

He was ten. He had the beginnings of a shell he could protect himself with.

And in time he would forget how it felt to be without that shell, forget how very wonderful it was to have no covering over his heart at all.

CHAPTER ☆ *4* ☆

☆

☆

HONOR ROLL FOR TOM

☆

A few days ago Tom brought home his report card. Since then—underneath and in between all the varied things which make up my life alone and our lives together here at home—odd little phrases, pieces of ideas, have been going through my mind.

Last night, in the dark, they crystallized.

Tom was disappointed in that report card. He had come toward the car, his steps dragging. He had crawled in and looked at me sideways.

I didn't have to ask.

I knew that inside the yellow oblong envelope he carried a handful of ashes, dust of a burned dream.

This, for Tom, is the year of trying, of beginning to prove, in channeled and routine ways, the texture of his mind.

Of trying to be like the others. He, born and bred so naturally a nonconformist.

The envelope then, held the lost hope—the hope of being on the Honor Roll.

He said quickly, in his tough voice, "I wasn't the only one. *She* said that probably we'd never get a worse report than this one."

So I knew how it was.

We looked at it and got it over with.

There was a great and almost hysterical relief in Tom because his father and I didn't make a fuss about it.

We just said that he was making great strides in concentration—that if he kept at it and didn't worry or get nervous, but worked straight and quiet, sitting still, and above all, listening, he would do better. He was a very bright boy, we said, only he didn't know it yet.

But just before he went to sleep, after the prayers were said and the light was out, he told me two things.

He said, "When they came to read off the names of the kids on the Honor Roll, I got all hollow inside."

Every failure I had ever known rose in my throat with that sentence and tried to choke me.

He said, "I have to amount to something."

I stood at the door. You don't rock a boy so big back and forth.

I said, "We all try and are disappointed sometimes, and then we try again, dear."

I said, "You will amount to something, wait and see."

A child limits us all, just by being young.

Because Tom is only twelve years old, I cannot tell him how much he will amount to, and the sort of person I have, day by day, discovered that he is.

Schools are full of all kinds of children.

The ones who will be businessmen.

The ones who will be President of the United States or the Kiwanis Club.

The ones who will be small merchants.

And the many, many, many, who must be engineers and scientists, if we are to survive.

All these are in Tom's class.

What is it he said of them?

"I know the answers, Mom, honest I do. But when *she* asks a question, I have to think a minute and there are always five hands ahead of me."

There are that kind of children.

They read. They focus. They remember. They sit in stillness and copy slowly and carefully. Their minds move quickly to a point. They are eager to show the precise and definite information which they have absorbed.

A teacher knows where she stands with that kind of children. A school knows. A parent knows.

You ask them questions and get clear, sure, absolute answers. Whatever your relations with such children, you know how to mark them, how to classify them. You know their place in the world, present and future.

Three Cs for Tom.

The teacher can't possibly know. The school can't know. I only learn, week by week, as it is revealed to me slowly.

Because Tom is Tom.

One day he will "amount to something."

But the things which will make him wonderful and special have no place to show themselves in school—in any school.

One of Tom's C marks was in history.

He's worked hard on history at home. But when the test comes, or the reciting, I ask myself, "How can he say it? The way he has to me?"

He stands in the kitchen, and he lifts his chin and puts one hand on a bleeding leg. He is cold and hungry. He stands in the middle of a battlefield in a tattered uniform.

There are tears in his eyes to belie the tightness of his blue lips. He limps across the kitchen, yearning one hand toward the departing figures that only he can see. He reaches, painfully, the wall.

He beats the wall, shock in his voice, and entreaty and disgust.

"Come back, you cowards," he cries. "Come back and fight, you dirty yellow cowards!"

He cries it over and over. Until his grandmother comes out of her room, worry on her face, to stand watching him. We both stand watching him, now with his arm against the wall, his face buried in that arm, his shoulders heaving.

We, too, can smell the blood of that old battle, and hear the cannons and see the black sky above the wildly retreating army.

"Come back, you cowards!" Tom cries.

And he is General Washington and his troops are deserting him. Alone, alone, in the midst of terror, in the middle of the kitchen, Tom is the one strong figure of courage—of America.

I straighten his room one morning. I pick up a scrap of paper. There are words on it, written in what attempts to be a fancy English script. I read them:

> Lord Cornwallis——I carry sad tidings. We have 500 dead and 53 wounded. Please ship cannon and equipment. We have just been surprised by the rebels and I am writing this by fire light. Please, for the love of God, hurry with the equipment. General Gage.

Yes, Tom got a C in history.

The night before the test he could tell quickly and clearly, dates, places, reasons, hows, wheres, whats, whens, whys.

Somewhere in the questions of the actual test, it happened.

With the pencil in one hand, and the paper held tight to the desk with the other one, General Washington came to live again in our boy's mind. The battle came, and the smells, and the feeling of all of it, the immensity and the struggle.

With their coming, their taking over, all carefully learned data slipped away.

To live in the past, to feel the atmosphere of removed time and remote place push in against you, cannot be recorded in words on a lined sheet of paper.

Not at twelve, it can't—seldom at any age.

Tom got another C. This one was in grammar.

That, most likely, ought to bring out something in me. I've been putting words together for a very long time.

I ought to storm, "How can a child of mine forget periods and commas and form letters so carelessly?"

Maybe I ought to think that, but I don't.

I can't.

I know how it is.

The ideas come quickly, eagerly, demanding to be said. They climb all over each other. They come out looking like hen scratches. Half of them get lost on the way because you can't write fast enough.

Tom must someday learn to type very quickly, as I did, so that his fingers can keep up with his mind.

No periods. No commas. Mixed-up spelling.

Yet, last year, in his notebook, there was a fragment of composition. It went this way:

> I used to think that the stars were fairies,
> That they slept when the sun was up

> I also thought, because I'd heard it so much,
> That the Milky Way was the place where
> Those fairies drank milk.
> Now I'm older.
> I know that the stars are not fairies,
> That the milky way is not filled with milk
> It's too bad, though.
> But——
> Well, I'm just glad that those stars will glow
> Forever in the dark night.

As I copy it now, I note that there are two periods missing and three capital letters omitted.

It doesn't matter.

"To walk in the ocean," Tom told me when he was four, "is a silky blanket, soapsuds and a mountain."

The last time his father went on a business trip, Tom slept in his twin bed. The dog lay on his feet and the light was out. The bedside table radio played softly.—Something by Proko-fieff, I think.

Tom didn't know I was awake. He started to talk with the music, a sort of chant. I lay there wishing I could write down the rhythmic words without disturbing their flow.

"Pharaoh," he murmured, "a long barren plain and they are carrying the body of the dead Pharaoh. Big birds lift and swoop around the sky and there are no clouds and only sand, miles of sand, and the sun hits on the silver helmets. Pharaoh is dead. The country cries in the sun."

There was more, through all the length of the music, more than I can remember.

To myself, that night, listening in the dark, I thought, "If there must be a choice, let the periods and capitals drop where they may."

The thing which troubled Tom most was the third C, the one in work habits.

This he did not understand. He has tried. For him, he has tried very hard—in school and, out of it, with homework.

Well, everything is relative. This year is better than last. Next year will be better still. His work habits are slowly improving.

But they're still awful.

Out in the garage is a chest, a huddled, muddled mess of a chest. It's an old trunk. When he saw it, Tom recognized it at once.

It was the trunk he had lifted up on the back of the covered wagon, the time he came across the mountains and the desert, to settle here in California around 1850. It was the trunk which held the handmade silver and the books and his pioneer wife's wedding dress. Tom fought and suffered for that old trunk.

When he saw it, he recognized it.

He put ten cents down in the Thrift Shop to hold it. He saved the rest, asking work from the neighbors in return for refundable bottles. Then he brought the chest home.

It was as if it truly came home, at last, to hold his treasures.

What strange treasures!

Scraps of cloth and worn-out cloaks and curtains that could be used for capes. Strips of ribbon to be wound around bare legs, Grecian style. Sheets from which to make the short toga and the long robe.

This year he doesn't go to the chest very much. This year, for the first sad time, he is aware of the people on our street, who might think it odd for such a strapping boy to stride in pride and danger up and down the alley, sword flashing, talking to himself.

But there was a time, not long ago, when he was supposed to be emptying the rubbish, that he would stand for an hour atop a ladder in the yard. He had a three-cornered hat on his head and a pipe of cardboard in his hand.

He peered through that pipe, again and again, alternately hallooing and holding rigid with fear. He peered across the waves of some great pounding ocean, atop the deck of some sail-billowed, pushing ship.

There was a time, and not long ago, when he was a pirate in a red corduroy coat (fifty cents at the Salvation Army store) with a hook for a hand, a hook made from the top of a coat hanger covered with gold foil, and a feather in his aunt's discarded Dobbs hat, and a crooked mustache of eyebrow pencil curled above his arrogant upper lip.

Inside the house, Tom is still these men of derring-do, and Zorro and the Western heroes, too. The rubbish doesn't get emptied the way it should, nor his room cleaned, unless I make a downright issue of it.

Sometimes I don't make an issue. Sometimes I make too big an issue.

I suppose that's natural, too, because I am not always one person, either.

Part of the time I am his mother, and his teacher, and his school. It is clear to me, in those times of authority, that he must be channeled.

But other times, I am Tom. I, too, live all those lives in all those other years with him.

Work habits poor. Poor indeed.

Yet, when Tom leaves his books, or the lawn-mowing, or the rubbish, and sits down at the old piano in our dusty garage, it is not easy for me to call him back to duty.

To hear him find his way, no notes before him, notes unknown to him, to a melody which haunts him, which comes suddenly sparkling into his mind in the midst of cleaning his closet—to hear him finally, slowly, carefully, fit a chord to match the melody—buries and defies the mother in me completely.

Discipline is a word strange to my mind at such times. The ache for all human reaching accompanies my boy's searching fingers as I listen.

So little time, I think, hearing him, so little time for the reaching, the searching, the finding, the chord's sweet resolution.

Tom has a phrase for Saturday. He calls it, "My fine uninterrupted Saturday."

Dear heaven, what can a mother do about a fine uninterrupted Saturday?

Tom lays out his clothes the night before, the only night in the week he is so neat. He is up before anyone else, even his dog, on Saturdays. He's quiet about it. He fixes his own breakfast.

He reads awhile. Then he goes out to that standing-on-end coffin he built himself, every board, nail, pillar, which he calls "The Club House." No girls allowed.

He loses himself out there in rules and plans.

Before the day is through, they will all be there. Yes, girls, too—and all of the little ones, the three-, four- and five-year-olds, in which our neighborhood abounds, at whom Tom yells but whom he never really sends home, despite his threats.

The multiple, miracle, dreaming activities of a free uninterrupted Saturday.

The refreshment of it. The independence. The growing of it.

One shining solid day with no routine, no grown-up interference.

Where are the work habits then?

By rights, I should go up to the school.

I should say, "Mark *me* C in work habits. I'm sorry. Mark *me* C."

There's a phrase used a lot nowadays—in Tom's class, his school, all schools.

"Emotional maturity," they call it. "The child is emotionally immature," they say.

Even when he is five!

Tom said to me, "The big boys in the class (heaven love him, he doesn't see how tall he has grown) call me immature, Mom. Juvenile."

I can see why.

When it's funny, he laughs too loud. When it's boring, he yawns and wiggles. When it's wrong, he storms. Sudden wild spurts of running energy. Abrupt loud spurts of vocal joy.

He said to me, "But I don't care. I'm only eleven. I'm going to stay eleven until I'm twelve. Then I'll be twelve until I'm thirteen. I like being a child."

Three friends of his have lost parents in the past two years. Every night, every single night, all of these months, he has finished his prayers with their names.

He has said, on his own, starting it himself and continuing it himself, "God help Drew and Hugh and Jim."

Once, a month or so ago, I suggested, "It's been a long time, son. Don't you think the boys can take care of themselves now?"

He said, "They feel bad for a long time, you know."

I was ashamed.

120

When the little ones of the neighborhood ring the door-bell, Tom sometimes snarls at me.

"If one more little face looks up and says 'Tan Tommy pway wif me,' I'll be sick to my stomach."

Yet, having snarled, he opens the door and looks down at the big upturned eyes, and he smiles his silver-braced smile.

He says, "Wait till I get my holster, Brad. I'll play guns with you."

And he does.

He's brought home all of the bad words, too.

He asks us what they mean. He opens his eyes, with a slapped look, when we tell him. Most of the boys use them all the time.

He won't say the words.

Juvenile, they call him. Chicken, they cry. Baby.

And still he doesn't say the words.

Testing the present to the brim.

Refusing to be pushed into the future until it, too, becomes the present.

Permitting ridicule rather than losing integrity.

I should be so "emotionally immature!"

Those are hard things for grownups and a larger prize for a child—a big fat A on any report card.

But there is no report card, anywhere, with such listed subjects.

Before Christmas, Tom spent a long evening with his grandmother in her room. He planned for the holiday.

She told me about it.

"I know there isn't any Santa Claus, of course," he told her. "But I'm going to write him a note and leave the cup and saucer and the cookies. And I'm going to listen for him. It's our tradition, Grandma."

Then slowly, deliciously, he lived with her every minute of Christmas—from the fruitcakes right after Thanksgiving to the cookies, and the two ornaments he puts on the tree on Christmas Eve, and the one present he's allowed before he goes to bed.

He put his hand, in memory, into the Christmas stocking and pulled out the small gifts, and planned what he would have for breakfast, as he delayed, in wonderful anticipation, the moment of seeing the tree, full-blown, trimmed and lighted.

When I went into his room that night, there was a piece of my best paper on his desk. I brought it out into the light with me.

On it was a pencil drawing of the Manger. Of Mary and Joseph and the Babe with a halo—and very strange amusing animals.

I'm going to keep that.

Last night I couldn't sleep. I lay in the dark and grew a little afraid with the picture that came clearly to me.

It was a picture of a schoolhouse. Pouring into it—marching, regimented, uniform—were hundreds of youngsters, each little mind holding itself ready and empty.

Empty.

Empty space.

Space, I thought—space and rocket and satellite and universe.

Soon, they tell us, we must train our children to reach out to other planets, to explore outer space.

That, they tell us, or this self-same space will be used by others to blow up the world as we have known it.

So, with the enthusiasm of Americans, with shock and

shame at not being first this time, we push mightily in the race for prestige based on the conquering of outer space.

We push as adults.

And we begin another push for the future at the lower and educational level of childhood.

So it is. So it must be.

Yet, lying in bed last night, I could see those children like sheep, and my wakefulness increased.

I thought of the news of the day.

I saw the marching line of children.

This time they wore heavy space suits and bubble helmets to protect them from the far reaches of space, the rarefied and radiated places.

I looked for my own boy.

Strange, Tom was in another line with other children.

They had no uniforms, no helmets.

They didn't stand stiff and regimented. They slouched, easy, relaxed, full of movement.

They had only the tender fragile thinness of their skins, the delicate dreaming perception of their eyes.

Not to protect them from any atmosphere—not to hold anything out—not to shut anything away.

Rather, their skin, their eyes, were thin on purpose, were tender enough and sensitive enough that the atmosphere might touch against them, might flick on their nerves, their hearts, their vision.

There were thousands like Tom.

They were space men, too, as surely as the bulked and inflated scientific ones.

Space of another sort, though.

Space which lifts high and stretches eternally, for Tom and those like him.

Space of the dreamers, the interpreters of life, the sensors of the unknown, before and still to come.

Space of the spirit and the imagining mind.

The functional brain, the scientific approach, the photographic memory, the mathematical deduction, all become increasingly important to the survival of the world—our world.

With horrible, unthinkable methods of mass extinction, the precise and plotting mind has become of greater value than ever before in the history of man.

We bow before it, encourage it, train it.

And rightly so.

But, in the dark of my eye, seeing those two endless lines of children pouring into the unfillable schoolhouse, I found myself praying.

Outer space, I thought, must never, oh please never, defeat and defy and bury the great tremendous reaches of inner space.

The Honor Roll for tangibles must never supersede the Honor Roll for intangibles.

All those children, in their tender, fragile young skins—the ones like Tom who need time to "amount to something," to discover the texture and direction of their wild, free-wheeling minds that fit into no slot and serve no pointed purpose—must have their chance, too!

They must not be crammed, jammed, slammed, into a space suit which is too tight for them and too bulky for them to move around in.

They must have their chance to stand at an easel and paint pictures to explain a life.

Or to stride across a stage and live a hundred lives in one.

124

Or to sit at a typewriter and put words together to lift a heart.

Or to touch hands to a musical instrument and bring glory to a listening ear.

I turned on the light and chased away the dark.

I reached for a piece of paper and a pencil.

When I was through it was morning. The sharp, demanding clang of the alarm clock rang through the house.

I went into Tom's room.

I didn't trust myself to stand looking at him as he slept. I shook him by the shoulder.

"Wake up," I cried.

I cried it harshly, against the thought of the words I had put on paper.

"Wake up, Tom. It's morning. And you still have three percentage problems to do."

I turned toward the door.

"If you work hard," I stated firmly, "and concentrate for a change—for pity's sakes, put your mind to it—maybe you can amount to something."

"Maybe next report card you can get on the Honor Roll."

It takes quite a while to get a book published, between the writing and the printing.

I'm happy to tell you that Tom had a high B average, and no Cs, in school last year. He set some speed records in swimming, too.

I'm a little worried, though. I do hope it won't take too much time from, won't interfere with, his dreaming!

PART THREE ☆

☆

☆

LOOKING OUTWARD

☆

☆

CHAPTER ☆ **4** ☆

HELLO, MR. SMITH

☆

Walk down any street.

Yard is joined to yard, and sometimes there are fences, sometimes hedges, sometimes no separation at all.

Men push lawn mowers or stand with hoses in their hands. Children ride tricycles, bicycles, pogo sticks and skates up and down the sidewalks. Women trim rosebushes or stand exchanging recipes or call to their young ones.

It is a pretty picture in the twilight of any summer's night. It is very American and democratic and suburban and wholesome.

Long gone, and not too bemoaned, are the days when a log cabin faced all directions of vastness, in plains so great that the approaching caller with his flag of dust could be seen for miles.

Gone, too, made into rooming houses or gift shops, are the big old homes with half a block of greenery and trees to give them privacy, a long curving walk, a porte-cochere, and a parlor in which the vistor could wait while the members of the household tidied up in the quiet secrecy of the second story.

Nowadays, riding on a freeway, we look down upon a sea of regimented roofs, neat precise little ant hills. Nowadays, we ride up in elevators to unbelievable heights, key in hand, to unlock the door of an apartment which snuggles tight against its neighbor.

We haven't any spread. If we sigh heavily we're apt to blow in our neighbor's face. If we bend our elbow we're likely to hit him in the ribs. And if we talk loudly, he will know all our business, personal and otherwise.

It's been said that no man is an island. It's been said so often that it's getting trite. But it's true, not only of men, but also of women, of children, of the entire family.

And it's more nearly true today than at any other time in our history.

Our lives are interwoven, one with the other.

So it isn't enough, obviously, to improve our home by looking only to the person we married. It isn't enough to try to understand and appreciate and hold the clipped, quick years in which our children are loaned to us.

We are also alive in an outside world, and that world can latch itself tightly against us.

More, the outside world can seep into the cracks of the walls of our home and have great influence on the air we breathe. It can, in many cases, be a minor poison. Or it can be fresh lively air, stirring the atmosphere, clearing it, cooling it, adding to it.

This is never more true than in our relationships with those closest to us physically—the neighbors to the right, the left, across the street.

Because, you see, although the physical closeness is there, the gaps in any other kind of closeness may be both deep and wide.

A careful, gardening old couple may buy a house next door to a gregarious, large-familied young one.

A studious, quiet middle-aged pair may live in an apartment next to a musically inclined family of four, each with an instrument on which he tries his talents.

Honeymooners, their illusions intact, may hang new curtains at windows which face on the house of a couple who have hated each other, and life, for a long time.

And each will influence the other, and each must learn to live with the other.

The truth is that when you buy a house or rent an apartment or share a duplex, you marry a street. You plight your troth to a neighborhood.

Whether this is good or bad depends on you, on your attitude, your resilience, as well as on the quality of that neighborhood. It is not a simple thing, this marriage. But there is no way of escaping it.

I knew a woman once who tried. Her home was a fortress. It was an attractive modern house with a neat yard and several big trees spattering shade over a lawn which seemed greener than any other on the street. The walk which went up to her front door was bordered on both sides by bushes, carefully planned to bloom alternately in all but the coldest months.

Yet, walking up that short path from the sidewalk took a handful of courage.

I knew from experience, ringing the doorbell, that there would be a stealthy inside stirring, a quick flutter of drapes. I knew that I would be kept waiting.

Sometimes there would be no answer. If there were, the door would open a pinched width only, too narrow for my foot, and I would be allowed the vision of a pinched face, no more.

She would ask, "Yes?" The upward inflection implied clearly that I was invading her privacy.

The mailman, the milkman, unaware peddlers and people like me, who couldn't say "no" to a round-the-block charity collection, were the only ones who walked between the bushes to her door.

It would have required as much bravery to say, "Good morning, I thought I'd just drop in for a cup of coffee," as it would to walk into the White House and ask the President's wife for a sweet roll.

I'm sure everything was beautiful and clean and ordered inside that house, but I've always felt sorry for that woman.

On the other hand, I lived in a small town once—on Main Street. It was the kind of town where is was a personal insult to lock a door.

I loved everything about it. The wide shady streets. The vegetable market right next to the bank. The Brandywine River, which moved sluggishly through a small park. The funny, lopsided hotel at the Four Corners. The gracious library with its old and leathery smell. The tiny white church with its pencil-thin steeple.

When I came home from the library or shopping or church, I never knew who would be making coffee on my kitchen stove, or who would be taking a nap on my davenport, or who would be arguing the fine points of Buddhism around the dining room table—or playing cards, or just washing up, or borrowing a cup of sugar, or rummaging for cookies.

A friend of mine even wrote the first draft of her first book in our bathroom!

I felt sorry for the fortress woman. Sometimes, at the other side of the pendulum, I felt sorry for myself.

Neither the house with an invisible moat around it, nor the one that is Grand Central Station, is home as it should be.

There must be, first of all, in our relationship with the outward world closest to us, a trying for the happy medium.

It isn't right not to speak to your neighbors or just to bow coolly to them in passing. Neither is it right to live in their pockets and have them living in yours.

As I grow older I think sometimes about capacity.

I believe there is in each of us a certain capacity for giving, for loving, for liking, for taking, for stimulating others with whom we come in contact.

Sometimes this capacity is as deep as a well. The love for our partner sometimes seems almost inexhaustible as the years go on and we become more and more alike and interdependent. The love for our children, which so clearly sees their failings and tries to remedy them, at the same time never varies in its steadfastness, despite all faults and all youthful mistakes. The love for our parents, which has been used for the years of our own growing, still remains sharply loyal and quick to defend.

We can draw consistently and deeply on love because love often begets love, renews itself, grows larger with use.

This, in a much lesser way, is true of friendship, too. Real friendship is practically always as great a gift as love—and equally rare. It is not to be confused with acquaintance.

Your neighbors are acquaintances.

This is not to say that occasionally your next door neighbor will not become one of your best and finest friends. My mother, in her old age, waits eagerly for mail from at least four women who shared a street with her in her youth, who know all about her joys and trials through the years, and who are now, when so many closer dearer ones are gone, her nearest and most confidential friends.

I carry in my heart a friendship which started in college, another which started during the war, still another which began when we moved to our present town. Each was born of proximity. Each has proved itself of great value.

But each was allowed to develop slowly. Whatever capacity there is, has been drawn upon a little at a time. Now it very much looks as if there will be enough left to last the rest of my friends' years and mine.

One of the things to watch for and to be careful of in a neighborhood relationship is a sudden, quick, "thick" coming together—as if you had met each other on a desert isle, after not seeing a living soul for months.

It has probably happened to you.

Polly is such a dear. She's in and out and you're there and there's always coffee on the back of her stove. She loves to talk on the phone and plan all sorts of things for you four to do together. She adds her stew to your salad and rolls and you all eat in the back yard every other night. She's open with her confidences and generous about lending you her best jewelry when she knows the boss is entertaining you and your husband.

Speaking of your husband, he takes to Jake right away, although normally he's pretty cautious about people. Jake is a golfer, perhaps. It starts with back yard putting. Then driving. Then the two of them up at the range. First thing you know, it's golf games Saturdays and Sundays and your husband is caught up in it.

In no time at all you are living Polly's life and Jake's. He knows how much money you make, what your husband thinks of his chances for promotion, his boss and maybe even you. She knows about the baby you lost, the fight you had with your Aunt Isabella, the argument you and your husband had four years ago which was so serious you went back to mother for a while.

One morning, if things go according to form (and they usually do), you wake up and wonder.

You wonder what has happened to all of the friends you knew before you moved next door to Polly.

You wonder why you've never finished those drapes all these months, what with phone calls and coffee breaks.

You wonder, too, why you don't know any of the other neighbors.

Underneath, feeling somehow disloyal, you wonder why none of the other neighbors seems to have anything to do with Polly and Jake.

Above all, with a funny little ache, you wonder what has happened to those long lazy weekends you and your husband used to have together, those quiet evenings of talk or reading or TV or going alone to the movies.

In short, one morning you wake up and discover that you have used up, quickly and far too generously, your entire capacity for friendship with Polly and Jake. You seem to see clearly a few things you didn't notice in your first infatuation.

You see that Polly and Jake somehow always manage to drop in the rare times you have outside company. You see that the other neighbors are friendly in a group while you have become a foursome. You see, through some instinct, some remark of Polly's, that you are not the first in the neighborhood to whom this sudden close huddling relationship has

135

occurred. You realize that Polly and Jake have taken them all, one pair at a time, at least those in their age group, quickly, too intimately. Then the whole relationship has collapsed.

And you remember, bleakly, some of the remarks they have made about the others.

Such emotional involvement, such intimacy, can sharply influence the atmosphere of your home.

Gone is your privacy. Gone is the lovely sense that no matter how small your home is, it is your own castle—and uninvaded. Polly's words, her ideas, her influence, and eventually (because it always seems to end that way) her interference, have changed the patterns of your lives, distorted them from what you would like them to be.

You have reached the limit of your capacity for Polly.

But perhaps your husband hasn't reached the limit of his for Jake—or for golf.

And there you are, with dissension in your home, and your husband, who has spent only leisure hours with the pair, seeing you in an unpleasant light and not agreeing with you at all.

A situation like this is much easier to avoid than it is to retreat from, as with the quick infatuated romance which burns itself out almost overnight.

When you have children it becomes even more important to work to achieve a good, but slightly reserved, relationship with your neighbors.

If you think the day when Polly turns on you (which she almost always does with your attempt to withdraw from the too-close interplay) is a sorry one, consider how your indoor environment can be colored and tainted by what happens on the sidewalks, in the street, on the lawns, to your younger generation.

Every spring, in most communities, the toddlers erupt from the houses, ready for their first taste of general living. It is a difficult time for the toddlers themselves. It is also a hard time for their mothers.

And it is a hard time for the people to the right and the left, and again, across the street.

These curly-headed or straight-haired, brown-eyed or blue-eyed, chubby or scrawny little darlings have a lot to learn. There is only one way they can learn it all—by living.

They do not know the meaning of a property line. A flower is not only to smell. It's to grab, pull up, and take home to Mommy. A hose lying coiled beside a walk is to turn on. A pet cat, sleeping in the sun, is to yank at and investigate. An older child, approached that first time with good will, who tosses a handful of dirt, is someone to hit with rocks every time after that. "No" is a word to storm at. "Please" is a word to ignore. An unlocked door is to open. A gate is to push. A stone is to throw. A tree is to climb. Dirt is to dig in.

If you are a parent, you know these obvious facts.

But Mr. and Mrs. Langdonefer up the street never had any children. "In my day, kids were seen and not heard and they had a little respect for other people's property."

Or Mrs. Frippit, who has six, believes every single word each one of her dearies says, and won't believe your dearie didn't start the fight which ended with some nasty bruises on both contestants.

Yes, if you have children, you can become acquainted with a neighborhood in a hurry, and it with you. To live in it, peacefully and calmly, is seldom easy.

It takes, first of all, considerable restraint on your part. You can start, by remembering Mrs. Frippit. You're lucky. You have nice kids. But just as they are not always wrong, so are they not always right.

It pays to investigate, to take time to find out what caused the trouble, not to rush blindly to your child's defense, not to make an enemy of someone who may still be living close to you twenty years from now.

It helps a great deal to start teaching your child, very young, to tell the truth without fear of consequences.

This is not easy or quick, and it demands patience and repetition. But in time a child will speak in honor, if from the beginning the consequences are somewhat lightened as reward for truth.

If truth is insisted upon within the home, it becomes much easier when the child starts his outside life.

It is important. It can be a great good thing, as the years go on.

There are times, not only in a neighborhood, but in school, and later during the troubled teen-age years, when circumstantial evidence may go against your child—when you may have to rely, simply and completely, on what he says. If you do not believe him at such times, trust goes out of you. Much more vitally, faith in your support goes out of the young person. This can sometimes be tragic.

With children, too, in order to have your home what you want it to be, you must have your own home attitude, your own standards.

The pack instinct is something we fight in our adult world.

Moral issues confront us every day. Whether we conform or not with the compromises other people make—in business, in social life, in religion, in intelligence—makes all the difference between reaching up to something better or sliding along to something worse.

In short, if we let Polly and Jake and their many counter-parts run our lives and change our thinking, our ideals, we are living by their standards and not our own.

It is the same with our children.

If Mrs. Frippit's eight-year-old is allowed to ride a bicycle all over town unsupervised, we hear about it. If Jim is allowed to stay up till ten, if Mark doesn't ever have to do any homework, if June can watch all sorts of TV shows, if Pat never has any chores to do—our own youngsters tell us about it. The expression on their faces and their mouths and in their eyes is seldom one of appreciation for the way their own home is managed.

Yet, in this direction, too, we cannot afford to let the neighborhood and its particular isms dictate the policies of our own living. We cannot, for our own sakes and the children's, be too friendly with neighborhood concepts in which we do not believe.

How to attain this is a real problem in many homes.

A friend of mine had an attitude that worked very well indeed.

From the time her children were very small, whenever she was forced to punish or scold or insist, she tried to tell them that the unpleasantness was motivated by the fact that they were loved. As they grew older she, and their father, attempted to make it clear that no supervision, no discipline, no work, no planning for the future, no insistence on rules of physical and mental well-being, showed lack of parental affection.

It was not easy, and the results were hard to judge.

But a few years ago a little boy committed some small act of vandalism that shocked my friend's six-year-old.

She came to me with tears in her eyes—and happiness, too.

"You'll never know," she said, shaking her head. "I feel so horrible sometimes, such a monster. I want to say 'yes' so much and there are so many things I have to say 'no' to. Then Pete came home and told me all about Mickey. You know what he said?"

I poured her coffee and shook my head.

"He said, 'The reason Mickey does things like that, Mom, is that he has one of those don't care, no-nag mothers.' "

I stopped pouring the coffee. For a moment we looked at each other, refreshed with the knowledge that the constant spate of words all mothers have to deal in, had managed to spill on the sort of soil where it could grow.

Living in a neighborhood, community living of any sort, is then a great education in human relationships. There are situations, as adults, as children, which must be avoided, restrained, negative.

There is, however, on the positive side, much that can be welcomed and can add to the joy of our personal home life, just because we live side by side with other people.

As you can learn to share within the small circle of marriage, knowing that it will improve the flavor and the texture, so can you learn to extend that sharing to include your neighbors—with identical guaranteed results.

It's much more than lending a cup of sugar upon request. It is giving your time when you are busy, your smile when you are somber inside, your living room to the caller when you want to take a nap, your sympathy to a problem when secretly you feel that your own problems are far more vital.

It means, too, as in marriage itself, reaching a little beyond your own circumference to see and understand those around you. It means not ever judging by what is apparent just on the surface, but by considering motives, pressures, background, before you shut any one out of your life—just as you consider them before you let them enter too fully into your existence.

It means making some of the bigger gestures of marriage, too.

Being a neighbor can teach us, each member of our family, the meaning of loyalty.

Let's start with the children again.

They have flapping ears for what goes on from room to room in their homes. They know when Dad is worried about money or dissatisfied with his job. They know when mother is expecting another baby or saving for a new refrigerator. They know when the climate of the home is stormy. And, sharp little people that they are, they often know why.

The meaning of honor, of family closeness, of privacy and loyalty can be taught to them by showing them that these knowledges are theirs alone, a privilege of family love. We can show them that knowing a secret and spreading it among the neighbors is turning their backs on those closest to them —that no moment's drama is worth letting down those who have entrusted them with a confidence.

This is a neighborhood lesson which will serve them well all of their lives.

It will serve us, too.

Not that we are going to run around telling our own business. We're much too wise for that.

But it is impossible to live with neighbors and not learn some of their private affairs. Sometimes they are entrusted to you, as somebody, torn beyond his strength, confides in you. Sometimes it is just rumor, like stories about a man who stayed out all night, or a girl—but how can I give examples? Within the short confines of any neighborhood, my own included, all things have happened. None can be mentioned without touching either a confidence or a rumor.

Our neighbors are like ourselves. In that way which is so important to full living, they *are* ourselves. They trust their personal lives to us just by their very closeness, by the fact that we can observe and that we can hear and that to look out any window is to see our neighbor's sorrow and his joy.

For this, we must have loyalty. What we know, we keep to ourselves, as closely as our own secrets. What they know, we hope, they too will respect.

If they do, and we do, there can be on any street, in any apartment, in any town or city in the country, the right and good kind of neighboring. It won't matter that lot touches lot, or wall clings to wall, or that sometimes it seems too near.

What will matter is that our children have learned to respect the rights and property of those around them; that they have made friends with other children of all ages; that even the most cantankerous of the neighbors once remarked, "He's a good kid, isn't he?"; that the boys take turns mowing old Mrs. Martin's lawn for nothing because she *is* old, and because they know she can't afford to pay them except in cookies.

What will matter is that when we want somebody to talk to, caught in a sudden sense of weariness or loneliness, there is a near path up which we may walk and be welcomed. What will matter is that year follows year, and up and down the street the hedges are only hedges, not intangible spite fences—and the relationships between us, one and another so very different in everything except the place we chose to live, grow slowly in depth and meaning.

We are then very close to friendship, if the years are allowed to move at their own pace and the capacity is not used up too lavishly in too short a time.

We are close to love, occasionally, too. The small children become the tall ones. We see them move on before our eyes. And, knowing them from the start, we are close to love.

With time, with care, with thought, with restraint, with no anger in difficult times, being a neighbor, having neighbors, can widen the horizon of any home, heighten its ceilings, increase its meaning.

I know that this is true.

One of my treasures is the Mother's Day card sent to me which reads, "To One Who Has Been Like A Mother To Me." Another is the kiss a bullet-headed young friend of my son gives me when he comes into the house. And on my desk at this moment is a ragged clump of degraded roses, yanked from my own bushes, but put into my hand by one of the new curly-headed ones, unknown and unthought-of and unborn when we moved here.

I even feel pretty good about the eight puppies in a box across the street. Each one is shining black with white feet and a white blaze. We both try to keep our gates shut, my neighbor and I. Nobody asked our Sox to fall in love with their Dink.

But the result of the romance certainly makes us feel closer to Dink's owners—more neighborly.

Anybody want a good black and white, strictly mongrel pup? Free, of course.

CHAPTER ☆ *2* ☆

THE DIRTY DOG

My father lived two lives.

The first was based on the great good innocent theory of the Horatio Alger stories.

This one ended before he was fifty.

The second had its foundations in triumph over the times, everything which was weak in himself, and injustice.

This one ended when he died, on a high note, in a few moments, at the age of seventy.

Each life was surrounded by a home.

Each home had security of a sort.

But the types of security were as different as the separated man who lived what had been—and went on to live what had to be.

Let me try to tell you about it.

This I have never attempted. It is not a simple matter to pull on any sort of deep personal experience and put it on paper. It is not easy to describe a person, to bring to life a person, who is no longer living and who, when he was, walked through your days in an aura colored by your emotions toward him.

E.J. we called him. Everybody did, even the men in the plant, who titled him simply, "Boss."

It was a word which pleased him, you could tell. His keen, dark eyes would light up in response. He grinned at the corners of his mouth, no matter how serious the problem. "E.J., the Boss!"

It suited him. All the years of my growing up, the initials and the tribute fitted him like the proverbial glove.

This was a busy, driving man, this E.J. There were never enough hours in the day for the work he wanted to do. There was never a sunrise which wasn't lazy and after his rising.

From the beginning, the whip was on his back and he loved the sting of it. It was incomprehensible to him that others might resent the lesser whip he wielded. All living had purpose and all purpose was work—work, the further effort, the climb.

In E.J.'s time you started at the bottom. You educated yourself. You were a "self-made" man. You went step by step and never slipped back. Everybody recognized your ability because you proved it before you asked them to look.

From a truck garden at fourteen, to a drawing board at eighteen. Nights were for study. Days were for work, for walking there to save carfare, eating handfuls of dry oatmeal because it was healthy and cheap, and carrying always a pocket of raisins for quick energy.

There were "college educated" men, of course. These E.J. spoke of with respect, no matter how trivial they were. It was his belief that something miraculous happened during the time spent at a university. If there was so much to learn, with a mind like his, from the courses which came in the mail, how much greater must be the knowledge absorbed by those fortunate ones during four concentrated years in Ivy Halls.

The young E.J. was not easy to live with. He was positive in his opinions. He was sharp and quick with his tongue. He had little tolerance for those sleepy of mind or body, for the weak ones or the slow. He had a goal set so high he couldn't see it, cloud-shrouded as it was. But he knew he would get to it some day. Each rise he came to revealed a higher place.

So he moved through the years. He had no help except himself. Not from my mother, who was lonely during his long studious evenings when he was beside her, but beyond touch at the same time. Not from me, who went along from selfish age to age, asking for what I wanted and believing the depth of my father's pocket was measureless. Not from outside sources, except for the aging engineer who saw in E.J.'s mid-twenties some reflection of his own youthful ambitions and coached him in his home, casually, a little condescendingly.

Him, E.J. enshrined all the rest of his life.

Horatio Alger stories *did* come true, in those days.

The work on the drawing board became the work of an executive. The pay went up and up. The office was filled with the roaring sound of the great plant and the sharp metallic smell of it. But it was an office, and there was a secretary. There was a war, too, the one to end all wars. Authority became greater. The plant merged with two other larger plants. The money rolled in.

There seemed to be no end, no limit to it.

It was a far cry from the truck garden. E.J. was not the one to forget it. He passed his success story along to all sorts of young men. He passed it along to me. But most of the time he was busy increasing production, taking his kudos and his prominence with a little swagger, but in his stride—and never for a moment believing that there was anywhere to go but up.

Out of this attitude there grew our homes, the places where we lived. There was the three-room apartment on the other side of town, where I was born. There was the flat on the right side of town where I went to grammar school. There was the bungalow-type house in the suburbs, from which I went to high school, with the playhouse and the tennis court and the extra lot.

By the time I was in college there was the big house on the broad lot, professionally landscaped, with big trees, a double garage (room for my roadster) and a maid, pert and sassy and in uniform, to open the door.

Nowhere to go but up.

Generous, enthusiastic, extravagant, egotistic, loyal—headlong into the future E.J. marched. No, he didn't. He ran there.

He pulled us all along. He paid the freight. He picked up the tabs—for me, for mother, for my grandparents, for other relatives, for friends, for strangers.

He was It. He was "The Boss."

If sometimes his sureness offended, he was unaware of it, and so were we. If sometimes his generosity was a matter of contrast to simpler, more sensitive people, he didn't realize it. He didn't realize that some took advantage of him. He trusted everybody. He trusted life.

I realize now that we, as a family, all those high-flown, going years did the same thing.

"Money doesn't mean a thing to me, not a thing." It was E.J.'s litany. He proved it. He threw it away. Nothing ever had more than surface wear before it was replaced.

We, all of us, had no more than surface wear, either. We didn't know what lay under the bright, tight, day-to-day living.

We had a home, a security, which reflected that surfaceness.

We lived at the top of our lungs. When we were displeased we showed displeasure. When we were angry we showed temper. When we were gay we laughed until it hurt. We were children. We hurried, like children, running from some restlessness, some lack, the presence of which we felt, although we never thought about it. We were in a rush to live. We were greedy to have, to own, to possess.

It still stands there, our material home, the peak of E.J.'s material success. After all these years, and all this living, I do not think even Mother, who once mourned every Persian rug, every tapestry, every chair, thinks of it as Home.

It was a house lived in by different people in a different age —characters we might read of in a book or see in a play. Not us. Never us. Could we have been like that?

Could E.J. have been like that?

Forty-eight, he was, and the world stopped dead.

They called it the Depression for lack of a worse word. It was a flash flood. When it receded enough so that the count of drownings could be taken, we were swimming feebly. We were swimming naked, all material possessions washed away.

Because we were so small, so rooted in our own egos, because the trick, the crooked deal, the final push, had been managed by someone E.J. trusted like a brother, I cried, Mother cried, "The dirty dog. The dirty, dirty dog."

"No," E.J. said, and began to shake. "No. He is a good man. He was just tempted—it must be something else. It must be my fault."

The first show of gentleness, a calm wind for all of us.

E.J. never stopped shaking, a visible tremble in his head and his hands. Strangely, and to me wondrously, he never said an unkind word the rest of his life.

Strangely, and at first sadly, we never saw the busy, driving, cocksure "Boss" again.

We missed him. We missed him very much in the rented bedrooms we called home, in the strange cold town where we moved.

You live with a driving force and you lean against the force all your life and let it support you. When it is gone, when the wind against which you are pushing dies down abruptly, you lose your balance and feel as if you are going to fall on your face.

"Too old," they told him. Wherever he went with his pathetic income tax statement to prove to them the man he had been, "Too old," they said.

He believed them.

Then it began to happen. As surely as a snake slides out of its old skin, E.J. stepped out from the boundaries of the man who believed that there was nowhere to go but up, the man who looked up only, through his own eyes and in a squeezed periphery.

For fourteen dollars a week he was granted the great favor of walking outward, of stretching his feet from door to door and his hands from bell to bell.

It was very hard to get, such work. It took a long time to get. When it came, when the hours were filled with labor again, new breath lifted in him.

So much else came into him that I don't know how to tell it.

First, with the selling from house to house, there was the

realization that the world was full of people. Somehow, in the Horatio Alger stories, the world is full of one alone—battling against odds, scratching and fighting and rewarding himself, proving himself only.

In the wide suburbs of the strange city, all sorts of people sat in cold houses that cold winter and waited for the ax to fall, to be next in line for loss.

"I'd rather," E.J. said, the echo of his youth edging his voice again, "be us, with it all over, than them, waiting for it to happen."

Wherever he went he talked with them. Slowly the realization came that he was not alone. That it was not his fault, all those material things gone. That he still had something to give. To work at. To survive for.

"Money doesn't mean a thing to me," he said, even then, even in the hard times.

I realize now that he was trying to explain it to himself, to us. Other things were more important. Being busy, being needed—these, beyond money.

E.J.'s hair turned white quickly. E.J. shuffled when he walked and his shoulders stooped a little almost overnight. There was that shake. He didn't look young any more. He didn't look vigorous any more.

He looked another way.

It was in his eyes. They were layered, velvet on velvet—way back in, the trust, then the guilt, then the pain. But thick and shining and overlaying all else, the new things—compassion, gentleness, tenderness—a blending beyond description.

We were a long time recognizing him. Too long, I sometimes think, in that regret which looking backward always engenders.

But the others, the outsiders, the people in the big homes they tried to cling to, the people in the little homes, the poor ones, they saw it almost at once.

He was just a man who came to their doors. All the rest of his life that is all he was. He rang doorbells.

For a long time he sold coal. For a longer time he picked up broken radios and tinkered with them. His shaking hand was so beautifully timed with its soldering iron that it was like the pendulum of a clock which hesitates dead center and accomplishes the marking of a moment.

One time he was ill.

That, I believe, is when we first knew the man we lived with.

Cards came, and flowers, and homemade cakes, and homemade bread. The phone rang all the time.

"Tell E.J. I expect him to get out here and rub my back by day after tomorrow, the old son of a gun." An old man in a shanty, we discovered, in bed for fifteen years, whose back was eased and his days shortened by E.J.'s visits.

"Your father's teaching my boy how to fix radios. I'm praying he'll get well soon. You see, the kid got into a little trouble —and nobody before ever took an interest——."

I wish I had written them down. But it would have filled too fat a notebook.

When E.J. was sixty, he sat in the microscopic kitchen of a three-room apartment fixed from the upstairs of a widow's home, and repaired a radio on his birthday.

His white hair was graced with a cardboard crown, worn a little tipsy, cut a little crooked by the widow. There were three birthday cakes. We crowded the tiny rooms with ourselves and our laughter, wanting to be with him, near him.

"Sixty years women been telling me what to do," E.J. blus-

tered, patting the crown. "Hand me the soldering iron.
What time's left I'm boss—king."

The word slipped in and out without any hurt.

Mother beamed at him. I put my hand on his shoulder
and hoped he would know some of the words I had never
said.

There was security in that drab little apartment such as
we had never felt in the big house. Never.

The ten years from sixty to seventy were too short. They
run together with living.

I remember a minute of them, though.

Two men were at our house, and E.J. and Mother and
some others. The men were very tall, unusually so. They
swung E.J. between them, against the wall—short, solid, still
stocky and a little round-shouldered, like a Mutt and Jeff
joke, flanked by the six-footers.

"Runt," one of the men said, not meaning to be unkind,
just full of himself and pulling tall for contrast. "You don't
measure very high, do you, E.J.?"

E.J. looked up from one face to the other. Suddenly he
seemed to be shaking more than usual. Suddenly, the layers
of his eyes shifted and it was with him, the superior time of
nowhere to go but up.

I screamed.

"Only one of you is tall at all," I yelled. "He towers over
both of you."

I started to cry and ran from the room, ashamed and confused.

I hope E.J. knew what I meant.

At his funeral we sat quietly in the place reserved for the
family, curtained and secret. There were a great many flowers,
a shocking amount. I noticed but I didn't think about it.

But when that last parade began, I thought about it.

They came up and they came up. They hesitated and stopped and looked a long time at him. There were handkerchiefs and tears. It was a long parade.

An unbelievable parade. Because when E.J. died, we had lived in the West only two years. I didn't know any of the people, not any of them, who came to say good-bye.

They were the people behind the doors upon which he had knocked—doors which had opened to him, while he told them all about himself, his family, his grandson, his old life, how much better it was to live widely in the world, and what a good home he had. The doors had opened to his listening ear, as the people behind them revealed themselves to him.

Yesterday, at the swimming pool, waiting for our boy to finish a workout, a woman came over and sat down beside me. She asked me how my writing was going. I told her, a little surprised.

She said, "I've known all about you, and about your son when he was a little boy. I knew your father. I'll never forget him. He was a wonderful man."

The tears were in her eyes, not mine.

My father died almost seven years ago.

To live in the world, to have a home with any sort of depth to it, any serenity, is to know that the world exists, and to share it, to realize how universal we are.

It is also to acknowledge injustice and cope with it.

Sometimes it seems true that the mean people, the unscrupulous people, the ungenerous ones, the faultfinders, succeed where kindly, warm people of good will fail. Sometimes it even seems as if they sit up nights trying to find ways to belittle, to spoil, to promote themselves and demote you.

This is particularly true in the business world. The man,

on whose shoulders rests all the security and much of the happiness of the home as a unit, has to face it time and time again.

How he faces it will literally make or break the home.

There is within all of us, male and female, young and old, a basic feeling that right will triumph. We're born with it. We're always surprised when somebody is unkind to us, or shows plainly that he doesn't like us, or actively tries to make our life miserable.

We're equally surprised when this "somebody" is a set of circumstances, or an economic situation, or a war.

This feeling of immunity is conceit, in a way. It is part of the cruel American myth that we are put on this earth to be happy.

But happiness, like right and success and triumph, is a word of complex definition.

If a man's whole happiness is going to be based on his material success, on getting ahead of the man on the right of him, the left, the one on top or the one below, the home he works for and the life he creates within it will fail. It will be a home of constant stress, continual petty worry, disregard for the feelings of those closest to him. His pleasures will be dimmed. The world he strides in will shrink.

These years we live in are different from any other years. Depression or no depression, war or no war, never has there been such a general lack of security as there is this very moment.

It is deeply imbedded within the nature of the male to search, sometimes in great danger and adventure, for permanency and sureness for those dependent upon him.

Today he finds in the many plants and factories across the country, the thousand offices, the multitude of huge organizations, a here-today, gone-tomorrow sort of job.

There are reasons for this. Little is built to last, to wear, and all is change. Much of our economy, too, a frightening amount of it, is based on government contracts, on preparation for war, for defense of our way of living and our beliefs.

Sometimes I wonder, a little sickly, if we can ever really afford to have peace on earth.

I wonder what would happen to all of the people in all of the houses across the country, if tomorrow Russia and China and all the rest would unanimously and joyously decide to outlaw war or preparing for war.

Lack of security, of course, in these times, extends beyond job security. It extends to the big threats we all live with. Huge indefinite shapes hover in shadows above us, all the unknowns and intangibles in fear and dread.

Thus, a man, a dreaming man, with dreams inherent in the very beat of his blood, finds that his long thoughts of tomorrow are cut short. He finds that tomorrow is a time not to be considered too deeply, lest it destroy today.

This he must face, must handle, must conquer.

He can face it in one way only. He can conquer in one way only.

Other men have done it before him. They have sloughed off old skins.

E.J. did it. He carried no thoughts of injustice, no "dirty dog," into his new life, to poison his mind.

Doors opened, by asking to come in, by offering to help, by giving of effort and self when he could no longer give of money.

Above all (and was it so different, then and now?), work to do as well as work can be done—whether it leads to the top, or whether it moves in one place. Work for *work's* sake —for the simple, old-fashioned pride in a job well done.

The Depression took the steam, the drive, the sharpness, the great horrible rush, out of E.J. Because of his attitude, it added more than it deprived. Wherever he was, after those things were softened, became security, became home, for anybody who shared his life.

If we can try to turn down the pressure a little, to use economic necessity as a blessing, if we can lower our standards to within our reach, and count someone's affectionate regard as more important than a new car, we can begin at last to make a home.

We can, at last, perhaps, begin to make a person—a living, breathing, sensitive organism who feels and sees and touches what is *now*, instead of straining forward with glazed eyes into a day and a place and a home which will never come, no matter how great our speed.

R.S.V.P.

☆

Webster has words for everything, of course.

Party, for instance.

"A number of persons [among other definitions] together for a particular purpose; a select company."

Do you remember the first party you ever went to?

The invitation was probably handed you at school. There were drawings on it, perhaps balloons, circus clowns, gaiety. It told the time and the place and most likely read "Birthday." At that age what was the sense of a party without presents?

Then, at the bottom of the page there were four magic letters, separated by periods.

R.S.V.P.

You asked about them. You found out that they meant, "Répondez s'il vous plaît." "Answer, please."

From that day forward you felt as if you spoke French.

When you were young, parties started with a heart pound. Dress-up clothes felt starchy and strange. Dressed-up, well-known children seemed unfamiliar and unreal. Walking to the front door of a house you ordinarily entered through the back, ringing a bell instead of hollering for Jim, and being greeted by a mother put you in a different world—more elegant, formal, exciting.

Social life, that's what it was.

Social, says Webster again, means "Pertaining to men as living in a society; inclined to friendly intercourse and conversation; convivial."

Those young birthday parties were convivial, all right. There was plenty of conversation, usually loud, even if sometimes, in the frenzy of a potato race and pinning the tail on the donkey, it became a little unfriendly with accusations of cheating.

But it was fun.

Webster talks about fun, too. Of that he says, "Mirth, drollery, sport."

Our childhood parties had those three attributes, too—jokes, laughter, great physical activity.

Social life.

It is important to a child's development, essential to a teenager's security, vital to a young married couple's growth, part of a middle-aged pair's fulfillment, a hold on life itself for old people.

Social life then, way beyond our usual thinking of it, influences the harmony, the balance, the adjustment of a home.

Many a home has foundered, or known real trouble, because of varying interpretations of Webster's three definitions. Party. Social. Fun.

No word, as no emotion, means the same thing to two people. A home contains more than two, usually. And therein lies the conflict.

In any home, there must be a clear understanding of what each person is reaching for in a social life outside the home, a definite compromise about that reaching, and rules to govern such activities.

There is much to worry about in each direction.

Take your family: Jackie is nine years old. Sally is fifteen. You and your husband are in your late thirties.

Will that do? In this statistical age of ours, is that typical enough?

Jackie first, and the birthday party.

I've been invited, along with my son, to a lot of birthday parties. I've given one every year.

Nowadays they worry me.

They start out all right. The little boys or little girls, or the mixed group (which is rarer at the sub-teen level) come quietly enough to the door, brushed, groomed, ruffled or suited. They are laden with gift packages, usually elegantly wrapped by a big toy shop, costing more than they should.

The birthday child snatches the present before he says, "Hello." Only parental restraint keeps him from snatching off the wrapping in a like rush. The present is put on a pile for later, at least until everybody has arrived.

The games begin. They are planned. They all have prizes. Children hurry so much nowadays, though, that they are used up in no time at all.

The food is served, on loud demand.

Some of the party tables for elementary school children would fit into colored glossy pages of the best home magazines.

Not long ago there was a cake as big as a wedding cake. It was decorated with pirates in icing, sea chests, sailing ships, an ocean complete with waves, an island on which a pirate lay stabbed, very lifelike red frosting blood seeping from his heart. The whole creation was surrounded with gold-wrapped candies, edible pieces of eight.

At each place bags of candy gold flanked pirate hats, swords, eye patches and carefully worked out meanings of each child's name.

In the kitchen a huge pot of chili con carne bubbled on the stove beside the cupboard covered with toasted cheese bread, ice cream, milk, pop and a dozen dishes of expensive chocolates.

The pretty young mother looked both happy and exhausted before the affair started. Two smaller children clung to her skirts and pushed into everything.

When I went back at the time appointed for the breakup of the affair, she looked exhausted only.

"Every year I swear I won't do it again," she gasped. "But then I forget and it happens all over."

I knew what she meant.

The house was a mess. Paper and cards were strewn everywhere. I knew from experience that the cards had not been read, in the frantic drive to "see what I got."

The lovely dining room table looked as if a horde of elephants had feasted at it. So much good food was left, so many crumbled hunks of cake and melting ice cream, that I was assailed for a moment, as I had been many times, with the guilty feeling of waste in the middle of a world of need.

Above all, the children were no longer children. They were wild, loud, rampaging little animals. They had run the fields and torn their good clothes. There was one black eye, one bloody nose and various unseen bruises. There were soiled, sweating faces and glazed, overexcited eyes.

They pounded out of the house, not saying good-bye, not saying thank you. They yelled at each other. They dropped, tired and cranky, into assorted cars taxied by thoughtful mothers. They were ready to be rude at home, to ignore their dinners as they had half ignored the richness of their party lunch, and to burst into tears on the least provocation.

It can be much simpler, with only a neat homemade cake and dime store prizes. It can be much fancier, as we sometimes read of, with a whole circus hired to entertain a big birthday party.

But is it fun?

Once upon a time, giving a birthday party meant learning to be a host or hostess. You stood beside your mother at a door while each guest was greeted in pleasure. You looked everywhere but at the gift in the donor's hand. You welcomed him. You introduced him to the strange children.

It meant other important beginnings to the social life. It meant more than the start of social graces, the "Thank you, I had a very nice time," the "No, thank you" to a second piece of cake, the "I enjoyed choosing it for you" when your gift was unwrapped, the careful reading aloud of the card and the name of the giver, with thanks when the present was opened.

It meant learning to try hard to win those games, but congratulating the winner when you didn't.

It meant shopping for that birthday present carefully, finding the one thing you were sure the girl or boy would want, paying for it from your own allowance. After all, it was your friend, not your parents'.

It meant learning to wear good clothes comfortably and being careful of them because they were your best.

It meant minding your manners as you used your knife and fork in public, without your mother around to frown if you made a mistake.

It meant searching for your hostess, if she wasn't right there, to let her know how much you appreciated her effort, too.

But your Jackie has a birthday party, or goes to one, and it's entirely different, isn't it?

Jackie's fun, even at eight, even at ten, can be used to further his knowledge of behavior in a world where he is on his own. This is true whether it is a birthday party, or going with another boy to the Saturday kids' show at the movies, or spending an afternoon making models in a friend's home, or dining in a restaurant, or joining his Cub Pack at a picnic.

But does he know this?

Very seldom. And it is our fault.

Modern mothers go in circles of effort for their children. They run a taxi service night and day, with considerable juggling in many cases. They give them "advantages" in art, music, swimming, tennis, dancing, all sorts of classes.

We make great effort for parties, too. We have something special, in atmosphere, trimmings and expense. We outdo Pete's birthday party, or Sandra's.

But do we teach as we go? Do we teach how to greet a hostess, for instance, by being beside our child at our own door when the guests arrive, and again there, to remind them of their manners, as they leave?

How are they to appreciate refreshments when they are too lavish? Or restrain their exuberance a little if we turn the house over to them and no rules are laid down?

How is Jackie to know how lucky he is to have a birthday party, if he doesn't help make invitations, or trim the rooms himself, or plan the games and share in the expense, or aid in the cleaning up?

There is a meaning and a purpose behind young investigation of social life that will set a pattern for a time still to come, for all social activity in adult years.

It bears considerable thinking about, doesn't it?

Then, there is Sally.

Many books have been written about the stress, the tender troubled emotions of seeking a first popularity in the teens.

Too often, though, they deal with clothes tips, catching boys, general charm and make-up.

Too often, some of the deeper problems are ignored, to be reported only in the newspapers.

A mother of my acquaintance, with two teen-aged girls, will never give a party for them again, and has refused to let them go to any such affairs unless she knows the parents well and is sure they will be right in the house. She has good reason.

Another mother of a teen-aged boy goes around in self-pride because she managed to give a party where only one boy needed sobering up.

Still a third family had to call the police to end a small riot on their trampled lawn, when they tried to entertain for their mid-teen boy and girl.

These are nice children from nice families. Each one of them planned to have their special friends in for a nice party.

But in our town, and in many others like it across the country, there is a sorry development known as "party crashing."

If your Sally wants to have eight couples in for dancing to the hi-fi and a late supper, does she, too, have to ask them in dead secrecy and make them swear not to tell?

Do they have to park their cars in various separated spots around the block, so that it doesn't look as if they were there at all? Do the drapes have to be drawn, the music muted?

Why?

For fear that the cruising uninvited will discover the affair. That they will march in on it in unnumbered hordes. That they will antagonize the invited boys to fight. Or insist on dancing with the girls. And eat the food and break the records. And make trips back and forth to their cars for the beer in the back seat.

Whether Sally gives the party while you and your husband stand horrified and somehow helpless, or whether she goes to one and you watch worriedly at a window until she returns safely, such things are happening.

No home can be a fortress, as we talked of before. We cannot forbid the fun and friendships which are so essential to the growing years between fifteen and twenty. Nor can we "go along" too much with the order of the day—not when it contains something very close to vandalism, very close to a physical threat, from the less desirable element in the schools and the neighborhoods.

One thing, as you see, grows out of another.

The lack of manners at the small fry's birthday party reaches its ugly culmination in complete lack of consideration, in invasion of privacy, at a later age. Many of the trouble makers are not invited because they have had their chance and muffed it. Dogged by a feeling of inferiority, they become the crashers, the older versions of the rudest and most unmannered of the birthday children.

"So," you say, "how can we be responsible for all of the other children who are not brought up as ours are? That party crashing business, for instance?"

I saw the answer. I was there, helping a friend of mine, the night that it happened.

There were eight girls at a slumber party.

There was fudge to make, talk to exchange all night, hair to be pinned up, each other's clothes to be tried on, confidences to be whispered.

My friend's husband was out of town. The two of us, with so many years behind us, knew a vicarious pleasure in the purely girlish atmosphere. We sat in the kitchen, listening to it, and sharing smiles.

Then, between one sip of coffee and the next, a car stopped with a snort, a thud and a screech. The porch was assailed with heavy feet. The living room door was slammed open. Fourteen big, gawky, loud boys were suddenly everywhere.

I was frankly frightened. I had read the papers. I had heard the stories.

But my friend walked calmly, a little tense and stiff-shouldered, but with graciousness, into the crowded living room. She made the rounds of the boys. Her hand was out in welcoming, regal style. She asked their names. She recognized those of some of their parents. She introduced them to me. She offered them chairs. She snared the two most awesome ones, excused herself, and took them off with her to make hot chocolate and pile the cookies high.

The jumble, the racket, went away somewhere. Proper dancing began to the record player. The two indentured boys helped my friend serve. Groups formed. Talk filled the corners.

After a while, my friend was at the door again, her hostess hand extended. She thanked them all for coming. She asked them, with utmost politeness and no condescension, to excuse her and the girls, because it was getting late.

They filed out meekly. They were tall, good looking boys, somehow straightened and groomed, bearing little resemblance to the mob who had pushed themselves in.

The slumber party resumed, undamaged.

Funny, that roughest boy comes to see my friend every ten days or so. He has taken over her roses, which weren't doing well. He tells her about his future plans. He says to her, with a "real gone" twinkle in his eye, "Boy, ma'am, if you were only twenty years younger."

My friend has the answer—part of it anyhow.

What you expect, you sometimes get.

It's a matter of boundaries in childhood. In truth, it's a matter of boundaries for us, too.

We're bounded by legality, by good taste, by experience, by conscience, by decency. And so must our children be.

These are boundaries much deeper than any social life. They are identical to those necessary to stand safely in the middle of a neighborhood. They are principles, precepts, standards and faith.

Like so many other areas of home living, they come right back to sit on our shoulders. They can be our blame, or they can be our credit.

If we don't know these boundaries, if we don't live by them, our children will not accept them, example being so far superior to words alone.

It will be a stormy time indeed, ruinous to any good home atmosphere, if socially we do not practice what we preach.

So now we must look, you and I, as honestly as we can manage, upon our own social life.

It's not simple to do that, is it?

It would be nice to be able to say that when you entertain

in your own home, everybody is delighted, full of good talk, good fun and good food, circumspect and well-behaved.

Are they?

It would be a joy to say that when you, as a married couple, go to a club dance or a friend's home, or out to dinner, or to an organization party, you are always charming, well-mannered, well-spoken, sober and enjoying yourself in open easy terms, with nothing to be ashamed of.

Are you?

Those are questions I would not like to answer for myself on a witness stand.

When I was young I worked in the newspaper and radio business. I have been to all kinds of parties, with all kinds of people. Like your Jackie, like Sally, perhaps like you, I wanted to get along, to be a social success. I made many compromises of which I am not proud.

Much is said nowadays about conforming—fitting in with everybody, adapting ourselves to all sorts of situations, being at home wherever we go.

We do not need to conform with a social life of which we disapprove. Better, as the old saying goes, to stay home with a good book.

You do not have to go to office parties you don't enjoy. Or serve liquor in your home if you don't like the idea. Or listen to dirty stories at parties if they make you shudder. Or swear because everyone else does. Or flirt, if you feel loyal and in love with your husband. Or sit for endless hours with people who share no interests with you.

If you do any of these things, any social actions which are against the grain, whatever they may be in your case, you are conforming in the poorest meaning of the word. Strangely, you will win nobody of value with your surrender. You will lose a great deal.

More, you are betraying yourself. Not only your ideals. Almost more deeply, you are betraying the hours of your life, the unexpended time which can never be retrieved and which could be put to better use.

It is not necessary for your children thus to conform, either.

Sally doesn't have to stay out till two o'clock at her age because all the other girls (so she tells you) do. She does not have to let a boy kiss her good night because all boys expect it. She doesn't have to ridicule the serious interests which are just beginning to intrigue her or the new things she is start· ing to believe, or call boys for dates, or cheapen herself in any way in the name of popularity.

If Sally can see you stand straight, independent, yet gay and popular, she too will be tall and proud and charming, her own self in every way. The people she wants will gravitate to her, attracted by her very difference.

Jackie doesn't have to be ashamed that he goes to Sunday school and doesn't mind it, that he hates to laugh at people with handicaps, that he doesn't like rough stuff, that he calls his father, "Sir."

Not if his father isn't ashamed of all those things. Not if his father is respected for being himself, without compromise to the unworthier attractions in the world around them both.

Jackie will have friends, too. Boys may ridicule what they respect. But somehow they always swing around toward it, circuitously maybe, but eventually.

Or perhaps you don't lower your standards—never have and never intend to! There are no "party crashers" or the other unhappy circumstances about which we have talked!

Good.

But there can still be social disaster for the home itself.

The members of a family, individually, can find themselves on a merry-go-round which whirls faster and faster.

What's more, it's a merry-go-round which spins off in tangents. It is held only by the home base in the middle, a place to eat, sleep and change clothes.

Sally is off to her activities. Jackie is off to his. Dad has his own social life. You have yours.

Where is the home?

For Webster's good, solid definitions to have meaning—for social to be "inclined to friendly intercourse and conversation; conviviality"; for fun to be "mirth, drollery and sport"; for a party to be "persons united together for a particular purpose, a select company"—there must be family sharing of those things.

Sometimes I think that everything is done *for* modern American children, but that not nearly enough is done *with* them.

I remember social life when I was very small.

I remember a night when my mother and father and I went to Wesleyville on the streetcar—a long ride to a small neighboring town. It was a small house, too.

But there were four couples and six assorted children.

The hostess was German. The bubbling smells from the top of her stove and the deep brown, rich odors from her oven are with me yet.

The table was stretched to the length of a bridge and took three tablecloths. There was china. There was silver plate. But there wasn't any room at all for flowers and trimming, because the great steaming platters of food covered every free inch.

As children, we sat together at the foot of the table. As

children, we were served last. But there was plenty and we finished it. We all, adults and young ones, groaned like the table when the feast was over.

The women corralled our help for clearing. Then we were free, while they took over the dish washing. Their voices rose and fell, interrupted by the chink and clink and sudsy sound.

We ran through the back yard, and around the front porch where the men sat with cigars, and through the small orchard. When the light of day quieted itself, the sound of the upright piano brought us all back indoors.

Those who could maneuver piano keys at all took turns doing so. The small parlor was filled with the sound of "Shine On Harvest Moon," "Kathleen," "Sweet Adeline," "Wait Till the Sun Shines, Nellie"—all of those and more.

There seemed to be a big grown-up hand on each of our shoulders, and we were allowed, encouraged, to join in, no matter how shrill, how flat, how mumbled our words and melody.

When the repertoire and the voices were exhausted, we were put to bed. Our shoes off, we curled up all over the place. On the narrow, scratchy horsehair sofa. In the big, cracked leather chair. On the floor before the fire. On an afghan in the corner.

The living room lights went out. The grownups headed for the dining room table. Shafted and colored, the lamps from the other room and the old-fashioned green chandelier hanging over the table moved in slow patterns upon us. It eventually stilled our whispering and our giggles to a half sleep.

It was weird and wonderful, that semi-slumber. Through it moved the strangeness of lying in a room with other children, the hum of the women's voices, and the secure contrapuntal thump and rumble of the men's. You couldn't be a child, in that darkened room, listening and half hearing, without feeling loved, feeling safe.

It is the laughter I remember best, though. The game was called Flinch. My parents and the others were demon players. The laughter, the mirth and drollery lifted to the ceilings and fitted the walls like the varied paper on them. It went into my mind and tickled against my heart.

I was always very happy in Wesleyville, in that small house —and in all the other small houses of my family's friends.

Leaning against my father, eyes closed, head nodding, during the long streetcar ride home, the clack of the wheels on the metal rails was overlaid with laughter. The jounce of my father's shoulder, as he carried me like a sack on the dark, late walk from the trolley to my bed, took the rhythm of laughter and held it through my whole night's sleep.

People do not laugh much nowadays.

They do not gather around pianos and sing.

Flinch is a game long gone, perhaps not even remembered.

Children do not climb haystacks on farms after a Sunday dinner for a half dozen families, or dress up and present little plays for the assembled and patient grownups while waiting for supper.

There are baby sitters now. There is what sometimes seems like a compulsive need for grownups to seek all entertainment away from their children, as often as is humanly possible.

In an odd, intangible way, children are being rejected—in an important way, one they can sense, one which affects them and seems like indifference to them, even if they don't know the word.

Yet—your friends have children. You have children. Your

husband knows people. You know people. Your children know other parents, as well as other young people.

Do you have to seek, all of you, separate social lives, distant from each other?

There can be, in a bringing together of all of these shared personalities, a new sort of cohesive social relationship—for you all, as a family.

Maybe it will take quite a jump to get off the merry-go-round which goes nowhere. Maybe it will seem like a lot of trouble to entertain children at the same time you invite their parents. Maybe, even, some of your friends will feel a little hampered in their freedom of speech and action with children around.

But it can be done. It can be a select company. It can be fun. It can be a party.

Not every time, of course. Age seeks its own age, interests their own interests, and "togetherness" can get a little thick and unhealthy if it isn't handled with discretion.

But sometimes, please.

Enough times so that Jackie and Sally get the feeling of entertaining with you, of opening a door with you, of fixing the table out back for the younger crowd, of being part of the whole, an adult world.

Let them see you grownups when your own discipline of yourself is relaxed, when you are easy and friendly and not taking life too seriously.

Let them hear you laugh. Let them remember it when they are older.

They will.

And it will be an "Answer, please," in great good sense.

CHAPTER ☆ *4* ☆

TWO WEEKS WITH PAY

☆

Whenever the news of the day, the children racing up and down the street, the pinch of the tax payments, the breathlessness of activities, the pressure of a deadline, the undercurrent snarl of mixed emotions, whenever they all tangle themselves together inside of me—I close my eyes.

Not every time, mind you, or I would go around staggering and blind, life being as complicated as it is.

But in the worst times, the times when I feel that big as I am, I am too small a receptacle for all that goes on around me and inside of me—I close my eyes.

When I do, I can feel a kind of greenness. I can stand and look upward to unlimitable shade. I can walk down a path, snaking through slim-trunked trees, very early in the morning, and stand on a small bridge with clear, moving water talking under my feet, and turn my head at a sudden rustle to see the impudent, tipped tail of a retreating deer.

I can taste a sort of salt spray. I can stand on a big boat, dipping in a slow rhythm, up and down and widely, and reach my hand to dark islands just beyond my touch.

When I close my eyes, weary with the glare of sun or aching with the sharp contrast of many black words on much white paper, I can rest on the narrow strip of sand of a small hidden cove. I can see the arms on either side of it fling themselves outward into the water, as if to say, "Beautiful world, beautiful life."

I can be young and in the Adirondacks in an old roadster, with the rain dripping from every pine.

I can be older and standing on the edge of the Skyline Drive, seeing below, in the gentle expanse of the Shenandoah Valley the peace that was bitterly fought for there.

I can be on Chesapeake Bay, with the smell of an old fishing boat strong against my nostrils, and white water from thousands of jumping, hungry fish needling up the sides of the boat.

I can walk the hard-packed, pure white sand of North Carolina when the tide is out and bend my head to watch the sideways rhumba hop of small sand crabs.

I can be going over the wide road that slips down into Newport Beach and reveals, in suddenness and amazement, the thousands of sailboats that crowd the rich channels.

When I open my eyes, some of these things, and others like them, have been absorbed through the pores of remembering, and their refreshment is back again.

Yet, like most of us, I have never traveled widely.

Like most of us, I have traveled fourteen days at a time.

Two weeks with pay.

All through the years those two weeks with pay form a parade of oases in the huddled, dry routine of the other fifty weeks each year. Each one spreads long with the experience of space, the great rare feeling of nothing to do but look, the unexpected rising of the heart, the frightened knowledge of self's smallness.

That is what a vacation means. That—and more.

It means riding today on wide paved roads, where the past has trod.

At Fort Sutter in Sacramento, we stood at a window and looked into the room where Sutter sat when they rushed to him with gold in their hands, and the West began to fill.

At Monticello we saw the dumb-waiter, the swivel chair, the bunk bed, inventions which were hobbies of Jefferson to lift him a little from the trials of being President of the United States.

In Canyon City we walked through the cabin where Joaquin Miller put bold words together which have lived far beyond his time.

At the Lincoln Memorial one evening after closing, the guard left us alone with our camera while he went into a back room. Then he turned lights on the figure of Abraham Lincoln, putting life into the marble, expression into the sad eyes, and somehow the echo of a voice on the carved lips.

In Virginia City we sat before a desk in a worn chair and rubbed it for good luck, with a hope that some of Mark Twain's joyful, sagacious humor and his understanding would seep through the old wood.

And further back in time.

Rounding a curve, high above the world, everything opened suddenly between great scarps of black volcanic rock and ash. In utter silence, a lake lay, unrippled and secret, between the banks. In utter silence, alone, no other cars, no other sounds, imbued with the feeling of evil in the quiet water, of long-ago death everywhere, we rode the high edge of the lake and knew that we were intruders into an age six million years gone. We knew, too, that very little would live in the lake or on the black and rusty cliffs, as John Fremont must have discovered when he found the place well over a century ago and named it for his friend, Captain Abert, before he left to find more fallow, friendly fields.

How many pictures, without ever a camera, can be collected during two weeks with pay.

It isn't always so, unfortunately. You've been on the highways in the summer time.

There are families, hundreds of them. The children squirm and cry, hot and wind-blown by the speed, the miles covered in ferocity by a jangled father in a bright, flowered shirt. Father seems dedicated to getting as far as possible as fast as possible, and getting back again the same way. Tears, sharp words, rush, and the everyday world sit on their backs, impelling them, leaving no residue of refreshment.

Each one wishes he might have stayed home, in a hammock with a tall glass of lemonade, and forgotten about a trip together.

Some do. Some go alone.

Separate vacations, they call them.

Their advocates will argue hotly for the merits of them. For men fishing, stag fashion, in the High Sierras or Mexico. For women playing bridge all day in the shade of a cabana at the shore. For children shipped off to camp for the summer with other children and trained strangers.

I would not, you understand, lift my voice loud and long in debate with those advocates.

I would, however, know surely that underlying any high-flown phrases about the importance of spending some time

away from other members of the family, there was a deep
rift in the family itself—seen or unseen, acknowledged or de-
nied vehemently.

Leisure, time to be your best and most rested self, is a
commodity of great value. It has always seemed a waste and a
wrong to use the only free time of the year away from those
you love the most.

All the other weeks a husband and wife have from each
other only the odd, tired, used moments of the end of the
day. They go into each other's arms all too often filled to
the heart with weariness, with worries large and small, with
the hidden threat of an early-clanging alarm clock.

All the other weeks, the children sit at the dinner table,
the racing day heavy in their legs and the lids of their eyes,
homework waiting on the kitchen chair, frustration their
daily portion, and eat too fast and speak of nothing that they
feel.

All the other weeks, they have from their parents only the
necessary, viciously repetitive discipline, which is impelled
by the constant awareness of an outside world into which they
must be fitted and for which they must be trained.

The school, the office, the plant, the bridge table, the organizations, even the milkman and mailman and elevator
man, get what is best of us—the new freshness of a beginning
day, the courtesy of friendly greetings, the neatness and
grooming of making a decent daily outside impression.

The sad fact then remains that within the home and the
family, too often there just are no free hours. The end of the
day, the homework, dinner, dishes, baths, get-to-bed-at-a-de-
cent-hour time is the only shared time that remains.

And it is the dregs.

Fifty weeks of the year this is so.

Separate and alone the other two weeks, the man can be greatly refreshed by outdoor living and a good catch of fish.

Alone, the woman can be browned and rested, maybe even prettier, from two weeks at the shore.

The children can be "adjusted" and more knowledgeable from a summer at camp.

The separate vacation can give them all a separate second wind.

But it cannot give them each other.

The leisure is used up separately. The routine begins again. There are, once more, only the dregs of time and life to share.

A vacation, for a family, can be like the honeymoon we all remember, if we were fortunate enough to have one. It can be a little time bracketed by love and by change.

This change is not only of place and scenery, not only of pace.

It is, above all to make it successful, a change, a deepening of attitude.

I suppose occasionally this attitude switching is automatic with the fastening of the last suitcase or the pushing of the starter to back out of the drive. With lucky, adjusted, already serene people, this may be so.

But for most of us, the preparation, even for pleasure, takes a little time. Too often we do not allow ourselves this preparation. Half of the precious two weeks with pay can be dissipated as we slowly, slowly, with waste of the vital time, take one week to get unwound a little, and the second week to wind up again and hurry back home.

But we can plan for it, we can prepare, during the other months, the colder evenings. Whether we intend to move from place to place or settle in one spot and stay there, we can read the bright folders—together. We can go to the li-

brary and find out about the area we've selected. We can pin-
point its highlights, in history, in beauty, in general interest.

Thinking about anything good ahead of time lights the
Christmas feeling inside us, sparks the "there's a great day
coming" feeling. Anticipation adds to, becomes a good solid
part of, our vacation.

We can relax in advance, too.

When we can't sleep, those who know tell us to start with
our toes, then our ankles, all parts of us in turn, and consciously tell them to let go, to be limp, to drop, drop deep
into the mattress.

It works.

It works, too, to tell ourselves that five weeks from now—
four, three, two, one, tomorrow—we are going to shut and
lock the doors of the house. We are going to shut and lock
the doors of our ordinary selves and the usual. We begin to
relax ahead of time, knowing that soon we will move slowly,
think slowly, speak slowly, and look deeply.

This does not mean only looking deeply at surroundings.

It means looking deeply at the others in the car with us—
and last, at ourselves.

The boy has grown a great deal, hasn't he? The round-
ness of his cheeks flattens out. Around his firmer mouth there
is a tickle of down.

He has grown in other ways, too. All the long year we have
not had time to listen, nor he to speak.

He calls the vacation a "guided tour" because things work
out so well. We know that he means a guidance beyond a
road map. That is a growth we had not noticed.

He sits in a restaurant. The syrup for his pancakes is gone.
He swings his head, catches the waiter's eye and with courtesy
calls, "Sir—please."

The waiter turns. For a moment he stands quite still. Then something rises on his face, yeasty, almost hurting. He hurries forward and the smile shines sudden and sweet and very white in the blackness of his features.

He has been called "Hey you." He has been called "George." Other things, too. But he has never been called "Sir" before.

But the boy did not notice, did not know, did not recognize difference. And that is growth, too.

There is the husband.

He sits at the wheel, not breaking any speed limits, not setting any goals. He whistles or sings one tune over and over. He makes small, silly jokes. He switches off the main road at any sign which intrigues us. He and the boy investigate all streams, lakes, rivers, letting time flow as the water flows, cool and easy, white and foamy, clean and clear.

For him, there are lines we haven't observed, and tension on the mouth, and new gray in the hair. But somehow, in that free time together, the vulnerable boy we married manages to push himself to the surface. The sight of him is all the more to be treasured, because it is so inevitable that he will soon slip back under again, drowned and lost in another hard working year.

For ourself, there is the long, straight look.

There is the feeling of distaste for the year's mistakes, the quick temper, the sharp words, the pushing away of loving overtures, the not taking time to see all sides.

Instead of New Year's Eve, the holiday time is for resolutions!

It is for more than scenery.

The cheap, shabby entertainment center on the highway calls all the cars to stop. We do.

Before us is an ancient fire engine, a museum piece. On it is a young man.

"Pete," he calls excitedly to a tow-headed boy of four or five. "Look at this, Pete."

He lifts the hood and gently and knowingly touches the engine. He swings himself up over the back and adjusts a make-believe fire cape over his wrinkled plaid shirt.

"Come on, Pete," he calls. "Let's go to the fire."

Pete doesn't move. He stands entranced before a huge toy bunny which twitches its ears.

Someday Pete will catch up, though, if his young father can stand still a while. Someday, in one way or another, they will go to the fire together.

We sit around a pool at a motel. We swim and rest a little, and we look.

Across from us are a pair so new to each other they might as well wear old shoes and cans tied to their shoulders to advertise it.

At one end of the pool is a girl, ready to become a mother. She watches her husband dive, cutting the water without splash. She smiles. It's as if she doesn't see him dive alone, as if he shared the water with their child in some short time to come.

In the patio restaurant a young family makes a small, important parade—mother and father, three steps behind their seven-year-old, and a baby in a portable chair. They all talk, all laugh. Even the baby wiggles its naked toes in delight and excitement.

We are there, too. We, the middle ones.

And pulling into the gravelled drive in a black car as polished as patent leather, neat, unbeaten by the wind, careful and old, are the white-haired couple with all the crowded vacations behind them—two alone once again, full circle and still together.

We have not noticed this chronology in a long time. It is a sort of motel immortality. It is all life, from beginning to end, for one night strangely and intimately together under one roof.

There are, too, the ones by the side of the road, figuratively speaking.

Once I sat in the hot sun by a stream in the Tennessee back country. It was very quiet, so still that the whispered plunk of the handmade fly on my husband's line was clearly audible as it hit the water.

Then I caught a dusty shuffle and sat up straight to look.

Coming toward me were three women. Each wore a shift so ridiculously like the modern sack dresses that they could have been the originals. Each had a sunbonnet poking a long ruffled nose out above a hidden face. Each was barefooted. And in each right hand there was a full pail of berries.

They marched, kicking up tan puffs, eyes as straight ahead as soldiers on parade, shoulders stiff and proud. They did not turn their heads to acknowledge my existence.

But when they were even with me, the nearest one slid her eyes so martially that there should have been a click.

"Be yew sunnin'?" she asked, high and nasal.

"Yes," I said eagerly, "yes."

"Good fer yew," she recommended.

The eyes clicked back. The dust puffs blew farther and farther away.

Strange, from such a concise conversation, that I should feel ever since as if I knew something about the hill country.

In the Ozarks there was the family, six of them, who made baskets. It took ten minutes of smiles and leading questions to get them to talk. Then there was no stopping the flow. We didn't get anywhere near our planned destination that night.

In North Carolina, back in the brush of the great, swelling sand dunes, there were the albinos, white as the sand, shy as small animals. They spoke Elizabethan English and had never left the brush for two hundred years, except one man at a time, to sell their handicraft.

In Charleston, South Carolina, there was the incredibly wrinkled old colored man, his hands swollen like cream puffs, his eyes gone blue with years. He sat quietly for his picture. He told us he had been a slave during the Civil War. As we were leaving, in a surprisingly young and businesslike tone, he reminded, "That will be one dollah, suh!"

So many others to notice, to look at, to talk with, to store up in the memory for leaner moments, or bitter ones, or weary ones.

In the heart of the redwoods in Northern California, there is a commercial spot advertised for many miles in several states. Here men have made a neat trail through the big trees, with signs and hidden speakers to educate the traveler. Compared to the untouched places, it seems a little wrong.

But toward the end of the walk there is a natural chapel. Great beyond believing, solid, unmoving, almost linked, the huge trees reach together toward the sky, up a neck-cracking height. Before them is a simple redwood railing and a plaque with a carved-out poem. The words escape me, but the meaning is, "Be still, look up, see how great is the glory of God."

There, in instinct, as a family, and not self-conscious about it, we found ourselves on our knees. We prayed not with heads bowed, but lifted. As if the march of our eyes up those great shaggy trunks tipped with blue sky could go directly to heaven.

That same year, in San Francisco, we stepped through the exalted archway of a great cathedral. We looked down the reaching, demanding pull of the nave to the ornate gold and filigree and color of the altar. We looked upward to the vast dome of the ceiling and through the intricate stained glass windows. And altar, nave, ceiling, windows demanded that we recognize our smallness, insisted on our prayers.

Two days later, in Carmel, we found ourselves closed in and quiet in the room where lay the sarcophagus of Father Junípero Serra. We thought of the man who had traveled the length of the long state, building his missions, caring for the Indians, praying, curing, and going on to do it all over again. Suddenly, prayer was there once more.

Two weeks with pay.

The pay is not the check you get without working for it. The pay is greater. It cannot be handled or cashed. It can only be stored, a savings account with annual interest.

Two weeks, talking to each other, with time and quiet to do it.

Fourteen days of looking together at the same things, exclaiming together at the same magnificence, meeting in mind and heart.

Half a month of discovering new vistas, not just in the country over which we travel, but in the unknown wider, territory of each other.

Two weeks of bringing to each day the young child's wonder for what lies ahead, and, as if amnesia had struck, forgetting all of the life before this bracketed time.

Each year when we pull into the drive and begin to note the dry spots on the lawn, begin to wonder about the mail and the many bills, see again that the back porch really should be painted, I say the same thing.

I can't stop myself.

I always say, "If I should die tomorrow, at least I have had this."

I don't want to die tomorrow. I hope I live a very long time.

But if I should, at least I have had those times which stay inside me—green, spacious, apart—to be looked at behind closed lids at any time of any troubled day.

You can have your separate vacation, with my blessing!

CHAPTER ☆ *5* ☆

☆

☆

"STAYS TOGETHER"

☆

On a wide street in Hollywood there is a huge old brown house. It is converted into what looks like a broadcasting studio. Outside it, clear across the front, mammoth lighted letters spell out a slogan.

It reads, "The Family That Prays Together Stays Together."

Strange words to read on that street.

It is a long, curving street. It boasts many big signs, brilliantly lighted. They reveal movies of all types, eating places of all kinds, still photography as big as signboards, tourist-trap souvenir shops, luxury interior decorating and beauty salons, and the dozens of ballet, dance, dramatic, diction studios which are such an integral part of the hopeful, crazy city.

The sign looks strange. It affects me as those words painted high on rocks in the majesty of God's untouched mountains, crying "Jesus Saves" in whitewash, always affect me.

It seems as if the mountain glory ought to speak for itself of its Maker. It seems as if Hollywood is an odd place to advertise God in big commercial letters, like the wildest motion picture on a theater marquee.

Yet I know, as that first reaction strikes me, that I am wrong.

There is great truth in the sign which proclaims that Jesus saves.

There is equally great truth in the one which insists that the family that prays together stays together.

I know, too, that the world is filled with millions and each tiny unit of the millions is an entity, to be appealed to in a million different ways. Anything, anything at all, which calls attention, blatantly or simply, shallowly or deeply, to the greater further truths of life is a good thing.

Anything which catches, for no matter how brief a moment, the worldly mind, which, even for a breath, makes it realize the existence of the soul, is a good thing.

When I think of that phrase, "prays together," I am a little embarrassed.

This is a hang-over from my childhood.

Sometimes I was caught in the middle of a family which went to its knees beside the table before every meal. While the food cooled, the patriarch of the group, a harsh man much colder than the meal could ever be, prayed. He prayed loudly, dramatically, his chin lifted. He prayed as if he and God were alone, treading a narrow way too rutted and lofty for the rest of us—as if they alone would share heaven.

And we poor sinners grew red at the knees, then aching and finally, blessedly numb.

Praying together as a family doesn't have to mean—shouldn't mean, really—this sort of long, self-conscious exhorting, while the other members kneel trapped and miserable.

It can go far beyond that, in a natural and real way. It can enhance the atmosphere of the home. It can forge warm cords binding person to person. It can set a sort of mutual goal created from mutual seeking.

It can, in its best sense, give meaning to all other family activities.

Let's start with the outside prayer together that goes with church attendance.

When our boy was small we joined the church of our choice. Mothers took turns caring for the nursery. There were toys and smiles. All the little children loved it.

Except our son.

He cried. Four Sundays in a row he cried.

It was an old church, beautiful, simple, small and not soundproof. The worship couldn't make its way into me, past the blockade of nervousness set up by those audible screams from upstairs.

The next Sunday we took him with us. He was fully geared with little toy cars, a picture book and half a peanut butter sandwich. We sat toward the back, ready for a fast exit.

He kicked the pew in front of him a few times. He whispered in a funny little hiss. He dropped one of the cars with a clank. He smacked over the sandwich. But on the whole he was both good and quiet.

The second Sunday, when the candles were put out, the moment their shine was gone, he cried in a sharp, sweet and delighted voice, "Now we can talk!"

All the Sundays after, the service ended with the piping of that phrase. We couldn't seem to prevent it. After a while the congregation expected it. They smiled and nodded. It was a sort of seal on the service.

He picked up other phrases, too. Under his breath he murmured an occasional word from the prayers. For a long time he said, alone or in unison, "In the Name of the Father, the Son and the Holy Goat."

We didn't correct him. We were praying together, each in his own way, each at his own level.

When there was Communion, because he was too small to leave alone, he walked to the altar with us. He kneeled and folded his hands and bowed his head.

Somehow it heightened the Sacrament for me when the rector paused in his serving to set one hand on our boy's curls.

That was a long time ago.

Most Sundays we dress as neatly as we can, the three of us. We drive to church, and park, and walk down to our places. We sit there, hearing, feeling, praying.

Our boy doesn't go to Sunday school. He tried. He says they don't talk enough about God there. Whether they do or not, I don't know. I suspect it gives him the hidden nursery feeling.

I do know that it means a great deal to us to have him at church between us, very still and listening, now that he is older. What he thinks, how he prays, what it means to him, we have not inquired. He must find his own way to his own belief, as we have.

But he is flanked by us, one on each side. He is flanked by our faith. At the altar, in the pulpit, he is faced by a man of intelligence, great kindliness, and beautiful simple phrases which we and a child can absorb.

That, too, is a good thing.

I do not mean to imply, here or in any other chapter of

this book, that there is perfection in the home which surrounds us. That there is never dissension, never worry, trouble, tragedy. That there is always smoothness and serenity and utter thoughtfulness. I am not an authority, even of my own emotions, my own thinking.

But we are looking, you and I, toward every horizon of the home. The *way* we look can color and clarify and give us a glimpse of the essence of what a home should be.

Too, many of the honest knowings written by people like me are not written through knowing only the best and the most perfect. It is possible to understand more deeply about love, or faith, friendship, neighborliness, marriage, home, life itself, because of the other side of the coin.

The other side of the coin is always in our hand. It is easily flipped upward to face us. To realize the value of the exquisitely etched surface on one side, we must admit the blurred, scratched stamp of the imperfect half.

Conrad Aiken, in his poem "Palimpsest," called this, "the dark note which gives the chord its power."

It is always with us, this dark note, this malformed side.

So it is not with absolute authority that I talk to you, even about going to church, as if I were the best churchgoer in the world.

I am not.

You see, nothing is static—not even faith.

Everything comes and goes. Sometimes it is good beyond all hoping. Other times it seems to crack into a thousand tiny pieces.

All human relationships are intermingled. They are so very dependent on all other human relationships—a blending of moods, emotions, thought.

Sometimes they come together and fit smoothly. Other times there are only sharp edges.

When our son was small, we lived on a very dangerous, busy street, with many trucks rushing toward a great city. To walk downtown with a little child was a real adventure in faith and physical endurance.

So Tom wore a halter. It was a simple arrangement, going around his pudgy waist with a wide belt and up over his shoulders, with a strap long enough for me to hold in my hand.

It bothered me at first. It seemed as if the child of my long desire looked like a puppy on a leash. Passers-by thought so, too, I could tell.

Yet there were great advantages. I am a tall woman. He was a short, chubby little boy. To hold his hand I had to bend in a sideways crawl. To cling to me, he had to stretch himself off balance on his not quite coordinated legs.

So the halter served its purpose. He was free and independent, balanced, able to run on ahead of me. Yet, when threatened by the curb and the huge trucks that growled the highway, I pulled sharply on the leash. The boy halted. I reeled him in toward me, safe, still on his own feet.

After a while he grew wise through the halter. He knew where danger was. He avoided it. The necessity for being hauled abruptly away from it no longer existed.

I think that God Himself has a sort of halter on all of us, individually and in family groups.

I believe that He holds the lead rein.

He holds it firmly. But we do not feel the full, tight stretch of it because He holds it wisely.

He wants us to reach out to the limits of our balance, to move freely in all directions, running and testing.

194

He doesn't want us to cling fearfully to His hand or the shelter of His robe, too cowardly to bear the noises of the world's highways or its threats.

Nor does He want us to run wildly into life, inviting trouble and danger and tragedy.

Instead, it seems to me, when real danger threatens He pulls on the leash, gently, as I pulled on Tom's, but with a sharp warning tug.

If we feel enough of those tugs, after a long hard while we learn to avoid the danger entirely. We walk uprightly and definitely, in such complete freedom that often we are unaware that we are haltered at all.

We feel close to God. We feel large in faith. We go to church regularly.

Then, suddenly, the closeness is lost. The bigness is gone. The steady routine is broken.

No love holds always in high ecstasy.

No faith, not even that of the saints, is consistent and constant in greatness and spread.

There are times for all of us, even those who are good beyond belief, when the halter seems to stretch so far, to be held so limply, that we lose the sense of connection entirely.

To those of us who by dint of great effort have known a true communion with spirituality, such lax periods bring a sense of loss. We are alone.

We go to church and none of the ease, the relaxation, the feeling of floating a little above our own weaknesses comes to us. We're aware of Mrs. Abernum's ugly new hat. The minister's very slight lisp rasps on our ears. Somebody in the second row of the choir is off key. The place is too hot. The soloist's tremolo vibrates on our nerves.

It is as if we suddenly are turned back, like a clock after

daylight saving is over, into a darker hour before that which we have learned of light became part of us.

It is an unpleasant feeling, a temporary falling from grace although we have done nothing wrong, we have thought nothing wrong, we have wanted nothing wrong.

We are simply disconnected.

The spiritual atmosphere of a home is very like this.

There is the time when the leash holding us within the home is tight and firm, tying us close. The leash holding us and what we believe and the church we attend is taut and reassuring.

There are other times when we, who were a family, become merely a collection of people living under the same roof. Prayer and church and faith recede, grow dim in our sight.

As a family then, just as individuals, we do not live on a constant high mesa of faith. We slip down crevasses. Sometimes we tumble over cliffs. Other times we lie down to rest, to feel nothing.

We must not be guilty about this, or ashamed, or worried.

The halter stays around us, seen or unseen, felt or unfelt.

If we take so little to church that our minds constantly nibble on small extraneous thoughts, sometimes it is better to stay away for a while.

Some creeds dispute this, of course. For those, my apologies for the moment, as I speak only for myself and for my own family circle.

For us as a family, this is sometimes the best thing.

Church is "the outward symbol of an inward grace." When that inner grace eludes us for a little, perhaps it can be restored somewhere else—by a picnic in the woods, by a swim in fresh water, by sitting still on the porch and watching the newest rosebuds or searching for the first star, or by reading a really good book.

Praying together is not always an indoor thing, for a family.

It is not always a thing of words, either.

Prayer can be a simple matter of appreciation and of extension.

If you hold quiet and think about it, you will know that you are part of more than a worldly family.

You will realize that your worldly family is a symbol of a far greater family relationship.

You can be grateful to your bones that you have both families to rely upon.

Having a home come into being is a miracle in itself. What if you and the person you married had missed each other, had turned a corner instead of walking straight ahead?

There would be no roof to your home, and no room in it, no house at all, had that mischance happened.

Suppose you had never known the miracle of bringing more life into the world. You would then be, as many deprived couples are, like the palm of a hand without the reaching, outstretched, powerful fingers of your immortality.

You are praying together—husband, wife, children—when you acknowledge these things and know that without each other there would be no whole.

You are praying together and bringing to your home its most vital, potent force when you also acknowledge God. When you admit that without Him and the halter of His love, His wisdom, His foreseeing, His generosity, the dwelling you build materially, mentally, spiritually, could not exist.

In too many homes this sort of mutual prayer, this mutual

197

admission of human weakness and need, is absent. The parents wander lost in the labyrinth of total materialism. The children wander lost in an unzoned, uncharted world, filled with love that has no place to go, respect that has no one to look up to. Both turn sour with disuse, and the word delinquency adds more numbers to its name.

We are born to search. Until we die we search.

What the search consists of, which direction it takes, what treasure it hunts is the prime obligation of the home.

The restlessness is there. Whether it is divine or not depends upon a sort of balance in the home.

Some search for the constant addition and exchange of material possessions.

Others seek forms of escape, a hermit existence in the midst of people or a giddy, wild whirl on the carrousel of daily living.

Still others dream of full security, of money in the bank, house completely paid for, living on a cash and carry basis.

A few turn to the life of the mind, losing themselves in words written many years ago in another slower, seemingly more secure era.

And some people look for an answer in a religion.

No one of these searchings is the answer all the time. No one of them is the answer total and in itself.

Our search is made up of all of these things.

It is self-discovery and education, social intermingling, security, mental stimulation, the basic need to give and receive love, with the fine sincere leavening of faith.

These are the things we work for alone, as persons.

These are the things we work for together, as families.

What we attain as individuals we donate to the climate of the home. What the home attains as a unit, it gives to the outside community. What the community attains, it gives to the world.

If a family prays together and stays together, the circle of influence ripples wider and wider with time. When there are enough families praying and staying, there will be a community of them.

When there are enough communities, there will be a world.

It will be a world like no other world in the history of man.

PART FOUR ☆

☆

☆

LOOKING INWARD

☆

☆

CHAPTER ☆ ☆

☆

TENDER AT TWENTY

☆

I know two men who are managers of retail stores. At Christmas time they are busy, bustling, cheerful, they and their shops filled with the joy of the season, the hubbub of many people, good business, bright lights and color.

I think they carry something else with them, too, at the holiday time. In spite of the fact that each customer pays for what he buys, it seems as if they must feel a little like Santa Claus, watching their merchandise pour out of the store to bring so much pleasure to so many people.

In January, though, it's entirely different. The two managers grow haggard and weary. They eat meals at strange hours. They don't get enough sleep. They say that they wish they were in any other kind of business but the one they have chosen.

January is inventory time.

Sober industrious managers, sober industrious clerks, start

at the bottom shelf and count and sort each and every piece of goods in the place. They arrange and rearrange. They see what they have in stock. They see what is needed to keep the store going another season.

They count up what they already have.

They figure out how to afford what they know they have to order to keep in business.

It is a tiring and a worrisome work for these men.

Looking inward is like that.

It frightens me a little, before I even start.

After the War, we bought an old house outside Philadelphia. It was said to have been the village bank some one hundred and twenty-five years before.

I loved it.

But I went into it with nothing but a big-city background.

So, I put all the foods in the ancient pantry, arranging them neatly on the just-washed old shelves.

The first morning I went down to get breakfast. I reached into the pantry for the opened box of cereal.

A rat the size of a fox terrier jumped past me, skimming my arm and leaving me goose pimpled from head to toe.

I shook for an hour.

Looking inward, which at my age is also looking backward, is something like going into that old pantry.

There must be some rats there, because I have never killed them. I don't know exactly from which direction they're going to jump at me nor how big they will be.

But the store managers make the inventory effort, so that they may serve the public and succeed at their jobs.

In the old pantry, we made the effort. We got rid of the rats and kept all valuables safely, tightly covered. We enjoyed our life and the old house.

If there is to be a marriage of lasting value, if there are to be children from whom we learn and who learn from us, if there are to be relations with the world in all of its facets—there has to be a time of inventory.

The first of January.

It has come now.

Perhaps it should have come on the very first page of this writing. But it has worked its way to last, and that may be because it is the most important.

Or it may be just that I have known, without thinking, that to look inward with you, I would have to do that hardest of all things—look inward with myself.

Let's take a breath, each of us. Let's go back, each in our fashion.

Do you remember what it was like to be in your Twenties?

It is not easy to remember innocence.

It is not easy to recall gaiety.

It is not simple to sense adventure again.

It is not simple to regain tenderness.

Yet, when we were twenty, these qualities were ours.

They were the gifts of material which life gave to us. We fashioned them, you and I, into a bright, swinging cloak to fly gracefully in the breeze as we ran to our future.

Contradictory as it may seem, that bright cloak was also armor. Light and silken, it was, strangely, impervious against the dangers which beset us. It was woven of all those qualities.

When I was in my Twenties, I was innocent—not only innocent in the surface way, although that, too, was true.

My life during a great deal of that decade took me into a busy city newspaper office. There I heard jokes I didn't understand and language which was shocking to me. And my innocence was protection against them both. They went in one ear and out the other, because I didn't want to hear them. There was no dark corner in me where they could lodge.

I had that kind of innocence.

But another kind, too.

This, I have found since then, is the important innocence.

This is the instinctive, sure and very wise belief that life is good. That walking down a street in all weathers is good. That tonight you're very tired and everything went wrong, but tomorrow is another day. That hope can be more than hope. It can be a sure faith.

This deeper innocence is youth's heritage to age, if we can retain even the echo of it as we grow older.

When I was in my Twenties, I knew the meaning of gaiety, even when there was little to be gay about, always when there was anything to lift the heart.

I wrote a story called "Marriage Is For Two," and in one place it read:

One day, so coldly sunny it was swallowing blue sky and frozen clouds to breathe, Mike and Eleanor walked fast, pushing against each other, down the main street of their town.

There was a secondhand store. Mike grabbed her sleeve. He pulled her inside. It was dark and dingy, with the smell Eleanor had always liked of old used books and furniture. The thin old man who shuffled up to them looked used and secondhand, too.

Mike said, "I want to see that tray of rings you have in the window."

The man said nothing. He shuffled, he reached, he brought back the little tray, the velvet worn to scales in places.

Mike put his hand on a ring. He brought it up to the

light. It was a slim gold band. Standing courageously above the middle of it, cupped by three tiny prongs, was a small round opal. It looked milky and gray.

Mike held it closer to the light. "How much?" he asked.

The man peered at them nearsightedly. He bent his head close to Mike's. "For you," he whispered, "two dollars and a half."

Mike hesitated.

"Two dollars," the man said.

Mike pulled his hand from his coat. "My pockets," he said, "have just two dollars and no more. So we'll take it."

The man picked up a small rag from behind the counter. He rubbed the little opal, round and round, gently and gently.

He said, "When you wear it, if you are happy you give to it a myriad of colors. Did you know that, young lady?" He handed the ring to Mike. He took the two dollars. He said, "Good luck to you."

Mike beamed. Eleanor did, too. They walked out of the store into the sunshine. Mike stopped her at the entrance. He took her hand. He slipped the ring on her engagement finger. Then he kissed her.

They started down the street together, slowly at first, then faster, then running—down the city street, laughing and running and young, with everybody staring, their stares turning to smiles.

Eleanor looked at the ring. The misty, creamy look of the opal was gone. In its place was an undulating riot of colors and something almost diamondlike in its white shine.

The little opal finally loosened and fell out. In a sandal-wood box somewhere, I have the slim band and the sharp prongs.

Surely, somewhere inside of me, there is also a tattered

fragment of that gaiety, that strong joy which propelled with such happy speed.

Adventure. That, too, belongs to the Twenties.

What is hard is not quite so hard when you are young.

The first job I won, in the Depression—and it took weeks to attain it—was clerking on the main floor of a large department store. I sold gloves and a center counter "special" on peanuts, and there were nine dollars in my pay envelope at the end of the week.

The third day I was late, caught in traffic. There was no time to go up to the employees' cloakroom. I left my coat and scarf and hat on a hook in the basement and took the freight elevator to my main floor station.

When the long, peanut-studded day was over, I went back for my things.

The cellar was dark, gloomy—and empty. Empty of workers, and more. Empty of my coat, hat, scarf. I looked all over. They were gone.

The freight elevator man called from his cage, "Come on, girlie, for Pete's sake, before we both get locked in."

I ran back. "My coat and hat are gone. They've been stolen, I think."

"That was a good bright trick," he consoled me. He opened the doors at the main floor. "You can kiss them good-bye."

I walked to the one open door, with the guard who checked us for stolen packages. Beyond him the rain came straight down, determined and cold and gray.

I started out the door. The guard looked at me curiously.

A voice yelled at me, hollow in the empty store. "Wait a minute, girlie," it cried.

I stopped.

The freight elevator man came up. He had a battered hat on his round head, a mackinaw on his shoulders and a black sweater over his arm.

"Wear this," he proffered. "You can't go out without something. Wear my sweater."

He held it out. I took it. It was slippery with grease. I put it on. The warmth of him was still in it, a dirty kindly warmth that took the chill out of me at once.

The guard spoke up. "I got a clean handkerchief you could put over your head," he offered cautiously. He pulled it out of his pocket, a red and white bandana.

I tied it under my chin. I tipped my head. I held the corners of the sweater out like the ruffles of a ballet skirt. I twirled.

The elevator man laughed. The guard joined him. I found my own laughter running to meet theirs.

"Good night, boys," I called, and threw myself out into the wind, the rain and the cold.

I could smell myself all the way home on the bus. A greasy, long-worn odor combined with a chewing tobacco smell from the back-pocket home of the kerchief. People stared at me, I suppose. I must have been a sight in my black dress with the frills, left over from better days, and the sweater and the bandana.

But I didn't mind. Somebody in that store had cared whether I got pneumonia or not, had cared enough to do something about it.

The whole thing was an adventure to talk about and laugh over, and somehow I would manage a new coat.

Years later, whenever I went into that department store, I rode the freight elevator. Pat, his name was, and he had a wife and six kids. They practically lived on vegetable soup.

I knew, because I went there for supper one night. I had a wonderful time.

Adventure. Remembering it, it had a smell, a combination of smells—old sweater and bus oil and rain and tobacco.

I am glad to sniff it, all this time later. I hope sincerely that I will always be able to do so.

In my Twenties (yours, too?), there was much tenderness.

The first Christmas of the Depression, I walked home from the bus in a slow snow. In that flashing way the mind has, other Christmases walked with me.

They were all centered around my father, Santa Claus without a beard. Extravagant. Lavish. Gifts piled to the ceiling. Every present on every list, every wish, bought and given.

The first winter it was not so, when I opened the door there was the smell of onions and hamburger, real as the light which hit me warmly in the face. There was the pine smell of the little tree in the corner of the living room—not our living room, but the one belonging to the maiden lady from whom we rented bedrooms and the use of her stove.

I walked in there and stood looking at it. It didn't go to the ceiling. It didn't even reach my waist. There were very few ornaments on it. But there was a string of red, green, yellow and blue lights, all winking. White tissue paper starred with false snow was crumpled under it. There was a star on top.

I stooped down. I rested my hands on my knees. I leaned my head forward. I studied the presents, wrapped in red and white tissue with neat bows, like a child allowed to look but not touch. I read the tags.

Four tags. That was it. That was all.

The muscles of my stomach knotted like a cramp in the

arch of my foot. I couldn't get my breath and I was too weak
to pull myself to my feet. I just stooped there until my knees
cramped, too.

My mother's voice called from the kitchen, "That you,
dear?"

Dad cried, "They're browned to a turn, kid. Get a move
on."

The big old kitchen was filled with heat. It was filled with
excitement.

I went over and sniffed at the frying pan. Dad stood over
it like a guardian Saint Bernard. There was an apron around
his middle, and Mother had tied a red bow in the forelock
of his hair which usually fell over his face.

The maiden lady was cutting butter into very thin squares.
Her face looked round and younger and ironed out.

"Your folks asked me to supper," she explained. "I told
them it was butting in, but they *would* have it." She looked
at me questioningly.

I was almost drowned in the wave of feeling that came at
me then.

For them all, in the old kitchen. For us all, the first Christmas away from home, but at home still, in some strange way.

That was when I realized that we had made an exchange,
our Depression-hit family. We had exchanged luxury, the
big world, the friends, the known, the outer, for something
smaller—something I sensed dimly, that would very likely in
the long run be richer and larger.

It was like trading a huge aquamarine for a very small
emerald. It was like throwing away the shell, so that you
might get at the kernel.

It was holding a full measure of tenderness.

We opened a door that time, didn't we? And I hope you opened your own door with me.

The pantry is dark in the corners, isn't it? But nothing fearsome jumped out. Nothing was given the chance to.

When we look back to those early years, straightening the shelves at the bottom on which all the other higher shelves must rest, we can see that what remains to keep us in the business of living for another year are four remembered valuables.

Innocence and gaiety, adventure and tenderness.

With you, as with me, if you have left the second decade behind you, these valuables are not rich and full-bodied, instinctive and positive. Not any more.

They are filtered a little thinner. They are watered down.

But they are there, if we look for them.

And if you are now in your Twenties? If you do not have to remember back years to find twenty-two and twenty-five and twenty-seven?

From the rim of my remembrance, believe this. Life will never be this way again.

Don't let any wind pierce the cloak you wear, the cloak woven for you and presented to you freely, as a gift.

Wrap it around you for warmth. Walk in comfort and understanding through the years of your first position in an adult world, your loving, your marriage, your parenthood.

Try to walk a little slowly, with no rush in your feet.

This is very hard to do and always has been. But there must be a moment to hold life as it is, just as there must be a time to count it out as it has been—before you, or we, grasp the future.

Don't pull the future toward you. Let it come at its natural pace.

Wear your flowing, dashing cloak while it suits you, while it is in style, before it must be discarded for more practical attire. Please?

It will serve you well, no matter what hardships you may know.

CHAPTER ☆ ☆ *2* ☆

☆

☆

THRIFTY AT THIRTY

☆

Down the street and around the corner, in a city where we once lived, there was the best organized family I have ever seen.

It consisted of a stocky, sturdy mother with busy eyes, a long, wiry father with fast feet, and three children—in high school, junior high and elementary school.

They had the most expensive home on the block. The lawn was always neatly trimmed. The paint was perpetually fresh. Wall to wall carpeting inside. Heavy custom-made drapes. A small grand piano. Television set. The biggest refrigerator, freezer, stove.

Sometimes I would sit on our front porch, shaking my head over our own summer-dried lawn, and watch them come and go.

That is exactly what they did. They came. They went.

They came back again. No two of them together. Always in movement.

The mother would head down the street first, in the good car, zooming to her good job as a secretary for an insurance man.

The high school boy wheeled by on his motorcycle next, headed for school. He never returned until after dark, after the supermarket where he worked had closed.

The thirteen-year-old and the nine-year-old were next to whiz by me on carefully shined and oiled bicycles. They came home after school, pedaling hard.

I knew what their hurry was. The teen-ager delivered our paper and all the others of a big route, and he had all of them to fold, all those collections to make.

The nine-year-old faced the tidying of the house and the starting of dinner. It was rumored he could peel a potato without the waste of a flake.

In the middle of the afternoon the father, in a roaring jalopy, headed out for his job as night supervisor in a big plant. Sometimes, when I didn't sleep well, I could hear his returning roar, well after midnight.

I was even known to reproach my own family about the integrated industry of the people down the street and around the corner.

"They make lists," I said. "They have bulletin boards. Everybody has his job to do. And does it!"

I started to make a list once. I was interrupted and never got back to it. I did buy a bulletin board. It is filled, this very day, with blue ribbons for swimming, an autographed airline envelope from a chance meeting with "Wyatt Earp," a "Prayer For Children" and pictures of pirates clipped from magazines.

The reason I didn't follow through, I guess, is that I spent part of a Sunday afternoon in that nicest house. I did it by accident, because I didn't know the people. Nobody in our neighborhood did.

You can't get acquainted with birds on the wing.

That Sunday I was on my porch and Freddie, the nine-year-old, squealed his bike to a stop when he saw me. Their phone was out of order, he said.

After I reported it for him, I offered him some cookies and milk.

"Can't, thanks," he said in a clipped, hurried way. "I have to get home. Ma's sick. Dad's at work. Sandy's at his job. Dick's baby-sitting at Dunbar's———."

I had to grab him by the back of the shirt to offer to go with him and see if I could be of help to his mother.

"Oh, I couldn't take your time," he said, his eyes surprised.

Nothing could have stopped me. Time, indeed, from a lad that size.

The mother was really ill. I gave her aspirin and washed her hot face. Freddie did dishes.

"I hate to take your time," the mother said. "I just can't afford to be sick," she fretted.

Freddie stood in the doorway. "It's time for me to do my homework," he stated. "Everything else is checked off."

The mother nodded. "Get at it," she commanded, "and remember, this is the night for polishing all the shoes."

They were certainly organized.

When I was leaving the mother thanked me. "You shouldn't have taken the time," she said. "I feel better, I guess. I won't have to stay home tomorrow."

Before I let myself out, I stood for a moment in the immaculate living room. It looked like a picture in a magazine. It looked as if nobody had used a chair or switched on the TV or opened a book. As a matter of fact, there were no books.

Books take time.

It looked, that living room, as if nobody lived in it.

As nobody did.

On the way home I thought, I bet they have money in the bank. I bet they're paying on a dozen installment purchases. I bet by the time they're out of their thirties they'll practically own the house. I bet the father will be head of his department, if he isn't already. And the mother one of these days will get an executive-type job.

I could see Sandy managing a supermarket at twenty-two, and Dick a circulation man at eighteen, and little Freddie working his way through college by waiting on tables or helping in the kitchen.

Those parents, I thought, are well on their way!

It's what authorities always say about the Thirties.

The important years. The doing years. The years to make hay while the sun shines. The years to prove you've got more on the ball than the next one.

The thrifty time.

The family down the street and around the corner was surely proving that.

But when did they talk together?

When did they think together—or alone?

When did they ever even have time to sit down and enjoy looking at the material possessions for which they were all exchanging those unrecapturable hours of their lives?

Where, in the careful plans, the steady breathless forward drive, the getting of shining tangibles, was adventure?

Where was the room for gaiety? Or the hopeful innocence? And tenderness? Poor, delicate, little tenderness, squeezed by minutes too busy for its growing.

That's when I discarded the list.

Webster says that thrift is "frugality; economical management; good husbandry; increase of wealth; profit."

Some anonymous writer said, "If you get what you crave, you're successful."

The Thirties are the years for all of these things.

But *what* is husbandry, *what* is wealth, *what* is profit and *what* is success? They are open to many different interpretations.

Above all, what you crave during these important years sets the direction of your goals and shapes the walls of your home.

When it comes to years to live over again, the old people look back, and with their looking, with wistful nostalgia, most of them choose their Thirties.

I choose my Thirties, too.

The family up the street and around the corner would choose them, I'm sure.

Would you choose them? If you are past them at this moment? If you are heading toward them? If you are in the middle of them?

Why? Why would we?

Because we, like those neighbors, run every which way in the chase for the exalted dollar? Because we are collecting more things than ever before, adding chair to couch and car to house to prove success?

Or for other reasons?

Remembering, I treasure those years because there was a war and we learned to be afraid and not afraid. Because the

war was not able to tear apart or destroy or minimize a closeness built up in our Twenties. Because there was a great deal
of strange new work to do, and we did it and forgot it and
didn't worry that the pay was low. Because time was shortened and capsuled, tomorrow was a word of terror, and today
became important, to be filled as abundantly as possible.

The old ones see the Thirties for many reasons, too.

They see the things which happened underneath.

A marriage found itself, shook down into a pattern, attained a solidity.

Understanding and tolerance came to life, a wiser fondness
than that of the Twenties.

Worldly accomplishment began, further ambition was more
realistic.

Parental responsibility was accepted and welcomed.

And the old ones see, from their sometimes lonely vantage
point, a house burgeoning with youth, bulging at the plaster
with growing, supervised by parents who are wanted, loved,
needed every breathing minute of every breathing night and
day.

It's not the pieces of furniture which are remembered in
later days, or cars or bigger houses, or money in the bank or
financial security or fine clothes.

It is a different sort of security—inward security.

To be organized as our family around the corner was is an
important part of the Thirties. Conserving. Acquiring. Se-
curing. Shoring up weak foundations.

But it is not all, as that family believed it all.

Some day those children will be grown, without ever having scratched any tables, or spilled anything on the rug, or
talked over their problems, or filled free hours with laughter.
What free hours?

And that is too much organizing.

The Thirties can be thrifty. They can be used to hoard and to increase wealth. But that wealth is nothing to be touched by any hand.

The anonymous writer we quoted added another sentence to his saying. "If you crave what you get, you're happy."

I heard a little story the other day.

It was about a church circle, a large group of women who were "very well off." In their midst, with nobody knowing exactly how she got there, was a younger woman, in her early thirties.

Everybody liked her, although her clothes were simple and even a little shabby. She had a small smile and a quiet voice, and she always seemed to have such a good time at the meetings.

At the beginning of the fall season, as usual, the president of the circle asked for volunteers to offer their homes for luncheon meetings.

Before anybody could speak up, the young woman said, "I'd be proud if you would come to my house next time."

They accepted, of course. There was a certain amount of buzzing among them about what to expect.

They were right, too.

The house was on the outskirts of town. It was very small and even shabbier than the young woman. They had to huddle and push and sit on uncomfortable, borrowed chairs and hold plates in their laps.

But it turned out, somehow, to be the best meeting they'd had in a long time.

The young woman was radiantly happy to have them. She greeted them with such pride and graciousness that it didn't matter there were only dollar throw rugs on the floor and not enough cups.

What mattered was that her husband, who worked nights, came through the back door, fresh from playing in the park, with three children so beautiful everybody gasped.

What mattered was that the young woman excused herself and brought out from the bedroom a baby with enormous brown eyes, an enormous smile and a gurgle, who let himself be happily passed around from one strange lap to another.

The older woman who told me about it sat in my living room. When she moved the diamonds on her fingers shot out sparks and the heavy silk of her dress gleamed.

"When I walked out of there," she said, looking surprised to find herself saying it, "I felt poor. I got in the new car Henry gave me for my birthday and raced home. And I didn't feel rich at all. There was something about that house —strange, isn't it?"

After she was gone, I got out my book of quotations. I found it quite easily. Robert Burton, 1577–1640:

"Cornelia kept her in talk till her children came from school, 'And these,' said she, 'are my jewels.' "

When I was in my own early thirties, in the middle of that war, I wrote in a story:

There had never been time for looking backward, for a recount. It was a bitter age they had been born into and the world moved fast and frighteningly.

You're brought up to believe that happiness is a goal, like a hotel at the end of a vacation's drive, like luscious dessert after a skimpy dinner.

But it isn't that way at all. The terrible thing about all

of us is that we're always on to the next thing, with never time to enjoy what we have. We never stand still.

I didn't realize the truth of those words when I wrote them. I do now.

The busy, frantic, rushing, hurrying, striving, bearing years of the Thirties are a whirlpool.

When you are in the middle of such a whirlpool, being tossed every which way, it's almost impossible to realize that in the center of every such circle of fast water there is a deep steady spot from which all movement extends.

This is the true center of affluence, the very heart of profit of the Thirties.

It is realizing how much you have—right at this very moment.

Happiness is not a hotel at the end of a day's drive. Happiness is the drive itself, tasted and enjoyed and stored.

It is not a luscious dessert at the end of a skimpy dinner. It is the simple foods which make up the meal, eaten in good health and with good appetite.

Sometimes, you know, the anticipated hotel can be old and drafty, with lumpy beds.

Sometimes the awaited dessert can be so rich it sickens.

This is what the old ones know.

Stand still a moment then.

Look, touch, taste, share what is yours—yours in a sense that no job, even at the top of the ladder will be yours, loaned to you as it is only for the brief time of your greatest efficiency.

What is most surely yours, right now, is no loan.

It is a gift. Given freely. Love from your partner. Love from your children. Friendship. Work. Health. Time.

Line them up in your inventory on the second shelf, all these valuables which the old ones look back on.

Count them out. See how they add up to increase your stock.

Hoard them a little.

That's real thrift.

☆

FEARFUL AT FORTY

☆

This year I have been allowed a great privilege.

I am teaching a little—eighth grade, twice a week. We call the course Creative Writing.

But from the first moment it has been much more than that.

To tell children how to write creatively, I discovered, you must first tell them how to think creatively.

"Look," you say to them, "you sit there, twelve to fourteen years old. Because you are young, a long beautiful life stretches ahead of you. Because you are human beings, there is a wide, beautiful world all around you, further than you can see or reach.

"Look," you say to them, "when you study, you learn facts. You absorb them with your eyes, put them into your mind, and speak them or write them back out as the teacher asks for them.

"Those facts," you go on, "are useful to the world ahead of you and the world around you.

"But there is another world. It is longer, it is wider, it is more exciting, and it can be far more beautiful than any other world."

They sit up and take notice.

"This," you go on, hoping they will understand, "is the great adventurous world of yourself.

"It is not," you continue, "what happens to you so much as how you feel about what happens."

You point at the boy in the third row.

"Jack loves to swim. He takes off fast, does a good free style to the end of the pool, makes a flip turn, and beats it back to the starting place. He wins the race."

Everybody grins. Good for Jack.

"But," and you talk more slowly, trying to make them see it, "the fact that Jack got a blue ribbon isn't the most important thing.

"What is important is, why does Jack like to swim? How does he feel, waiting to be called up? How do the muscles of his legs feel, his toes tensed around the edge of the pool? How does the starting gun sound, loud and cracking in his ears? How does the water feel, rushing smoothly up to him? His heart beating? His arms pulling? His feet rhythmic? How does the world look, quickly upside down with that flip turn? And the go-man-go race back home. Never looking to right or left. Swimming his own race all the way. Not knowing, until he lifts and touches and looks, whether he has won or not? How does that feel?"

You're beginning to get them now.

"Two parallel lives we lead," you tell them. "Two lines, straight as a surveyor's.

"The first is the get up, get dressed, eat breakfast, go to school, study, answer questions, play games, come home, change clothes, do homework, eat dinner, finish homework, watch TV maybe, take a shower, go to bed—life.

"The second is the constant, perpetual, hidden, secret and beautiful, stream of consciousness life, with the mind which never sleeps, the thoughts which never form neatly into sentences, the dreams, the whimsies—the self."

You should see their eyes shine when they find out that they are not alone in this private life.

We have tried to remember in this class, back to the first experience which touched so sharply against the mind that it can be recalled. We have tried to sit with pencils in hand and put down all of the rambling, undercurrent thoughts which drift through the mind, disregarding their quality and all punctuation—just trying to catch them, butterflies that they are.

To look inward then, is this, too—this search for what is evanescent, ego, hidden.

And the eighth graders go at it with a will, almost with a joy, searching back to when they were two or three, or even less.

"I remember a huge ball of fire on a lot of water."

Deke's first recalled sunset on the ocean.

"I remember riding on my father's shoulders, up so many steps they seemed to reach the sky."

John's babyhood trip to bed.

They don't have far to reach back, nearer the beginning as they are. What they remember today often will be completely gone by the time they are forty.

It's too bad. It's very nearly sad.

Because at forty, when the fear first begins, we need, more

than at any other time, to hold to us the thought that it is not what happens, but how we feel about it. We need to believe that the second life, the hidden perpetual life of the private mind, is worth something and has been enriched with the years.

We don't though, do we?

One of our best American comedians long stayed a constant thirty-nine.

He stayed at that year which won't admit new figures because it amused his audience. And it did something else, too.

It made him one of us.

We laughed because we knew how he felt, or was pretending to feel. It's reader identification, only visual.

Thirty-nine sounds fine and dandy. Forty sounds terrible.

In the course of a lifetime of reading, I've hit upon one scene close to a hundred times. It goes, with variations, like this:

"She sat before her mirror, brushing her long hair. The early morning sun shot a brilliant finger at her, illuminating her face.

"Suddenly she leaned forward, peering close to the glass. They were there! Suddenly, shockingly, dozens of them! Gray strands in the glossy blackness of her hair.

"She put her hands over her face, and moved her head back and forth miserably. Then, with great courage, she lifted her chin and looked again.

"Around the eyes, around the mouth, the fine sprays of wrinkles were beginning to etch themselves. She sat, numb, caught in the illusion of age. She saw herself for one frightening bit of time, sagging around the mouth, dark under the eyes, lined on the forehead.

"Overlaid on the image, she sensed the frail, withered ghost of a time to come.

" 'Forty,' she muttered desperately. 'Forty,' she sobbed."

It sounds silly, doesn't it?

But it, or something like it, comes to all of us. And we acknowledge it, one way or another—but never, not ever, with welcome and pleasure, as an honored guest.

It seems a shameful admission to make about us, but I do believe that if we had our way completely, we would stay thirty-nine forever.

Or even better, like the radio heroine, we would find romance at thirty-five or over—for some twenty solid years, every Monday through Friday.

Why? Why do we feel this way?

Primarily, I suppose, because there is such a violent accent, such a barrage of pressure, upon the glory of youth in America—not only upon youth itself, but upon staying youthful forever and ever, and well beyond.

Superficial attractiveness, lack of wrinkles, lack of expression, lack of bulges, lack of weariness, lack of nervousness—it comes at us from all directions, in all sorts of advertisements, television, articles.

If we would give to the development of our personalities, the stretch of our minds, the growth of our spirits, the search for our inner selves, if we would give just half the time and attention and thought we, as women, give to the waves of our hair, the creams on our faces, the uplift of our bosoms and the balancing of our diet—there would be a revolution of sorts.

We would be so gracious, so filled with realness, so serene in self-understanding, so well-read and even wise that we would pull everybody, even our husbands of years, to us and hold them tight.

And nobody would notice whether we plucked our eye brows to a flawless seductive arc, used "Worship Me" nail polish and lipstick, or weighed twenty pounds more than we should.

Not that we can, or will, do it, mind you.

I'm in my forties and I'm a woman and I know. Right now I'm hungry from having one unsalted boiled egg for break-fast, there's cream on my face because we're going out to-night, and in an hour and a half I have an appointment to have my hair done.

What I'll contribute (beside good grooming) to the con-versation and the party this evening is problematical. I've been very busy with my own pursuits, haven't watched a television program in weeks, have hardly read a newspaper, haven't seen a movie in a year, and there are three books on the coffee table, virgin pure and unread.

Seriously, though. Up to the Forties, men or women, the inventory of our shelves is almost all addition. We add up all of the things we treasure or manage to cultivate. We find there are a lot of them. We know there is a great deal of time ahead of us to order more stock.

The shelf of the Forties, right from the start, is a little different.

It is partially stocked with some goods that are slightly spoiled. They must be cleared away.

First is this fear, as youth seems behind us. We have now lived, probably, longer than we have yet to live.

Beside it there is another knowledge. We may have reached

our nearer horizons, but the far ones of our younger dreams are still foggy in the distance.

And we begin to see that our abilities were never as great as we once hoped they would be.

And last, there is the little broken music box which plays out the whir of the days, shorter years, seasons running a relay race more quickly than ever before.

If we can see these things and take them off the shelf, we can destroy them before they destroy us. We can manage to sail through the Forties and enjoy those years.

But a great many of us don't.

Take that couple you met on your vacation.

Weren't they the gay ones?

She danced through the night on high-heeled shoes with ankle straps, in great full skirts with a half dozen girlish petti-coats and blouses with ruffles of Spanish lace.

He played golf, in silky-looking slacks and cashmere sweaters, and did fancy dives from the high board, and wore Bermudas for the putting tournament, and half killed himself trying to learn how to sail a small boat.

And above her pretty, youthful dress, her face rose like a worn and battered prize fighter's under its careful make-up. Her red hair was a shade never devised by the biology of humanity.

And above the trunks, or the slacks or the Bermudas, his solid paunch pushed itself out toward the world, and the circles under his eyes belied his carefree grin.

Both of them, speaking of eyes, let theirs roam in all directions, preferably toward pretty young girls and tall handsome young men.

You felt sorry for them, and embarrassed, and you didn't exactly know why.

"The dangerous age," you murmured perhaps.

And so it is.

The vacation couple, you see, is trying to wrap that youthful flying cloak of the Twenties around them, to run fast enough so that it will float with some grace.

But it's too tight to wrap. It hangs limp in dead air. It does not fit any more. The material of it is too flimsy to protect them. It tears in their hands.

They need a warm, tight-woven coat in the Forties—not a garment far too young and gaudy to suit them.

The dangerous age.

Newspapers, books, stories, the divorce courts too often give the account of these years. They all tell of one general feeling—the nasty sensation that we have missed something.

Too many, propelled by this emotion, move suddenly crashward in their lives, imbued with the idea that somewhere along the line that which was intangible and lovely beyond expression slipped away from them without their knowing it.

So they try to catch it. From the outside world, they reach to grasp and grab. They change partners as casually as a square dance. They drink too much. They squander their earnings of common sense. They live in an adolescent world of emotional sway.

It's a dizzy world and an unrewarding and often tragic one.

It's not safe to look around too much in the Forties. Not even those closest to us can bear much scrutiny at this time.

Our children have grown tall and independent, and to look at them is to feel older, used up, our vocation outmoded.

Our partner is tired, a little gray, a little lined, and probably a little short-tempered, and to look at him (or her) is to feel the contrast that breaks the heart, to remember when we were both so young, fresh, forward-looking together, that era ago.

Just as for the eighth graders, there's nothing for the Forties but to look inside.

If it is done with an equal good will, an equal open trying, quite a few surprise packages can be waiting for us to put on the shelf.

Inside us is the proven understanding of many words which were not in our vocabulary when we were young.

Compromise. Patience. Close horizons. Comfort. Safety. Accomplishment. Time for more. Health. Balance. Mental authority.

You can make your own list.

We'll find, I believe, that any list will add up to a respectable whole, that we are much more safely anchored to living than we thought.

The pain of the Forties is real, compounded as it is of the realities slapped against us with the passing of youth. Like physical pain, though, if it is borne with patience, with some degree of courage, with quiet closed lips, with a little pride and dignity and a strong mind, it will heal of itself.

It's a juggling of values, at a time when our hands are pretty shaky.

But we have one consolation.

We are not alone in our juggling. Never alone.

Personally, I'm still working on it.

CHAPTER ☆ *4* ☆

DUST AT FIFTY

☆

It would be an experiment almost worth the trying to make a book of all the people who have walked through my life, gallantly, with half a hundred years written on their faces and in their gaits.

All different, so different.

There was the woman with the crazy flyaway hair, who rented us her lovely big apartment for much less than it was worth, when she needed every penny it could have brought from wealthier tenants.

I remember her nose—a fine, proud hawk of a bone standing out over her generous mouth—and the way she carried herself, because once when she was young she had been a model.

What I remember most, of course, is why she let us have the place so cheaply.

"I'm lonesome," she said. "I'd rather have folks like you all around than eat."

I believe that's exactly the way it worked out.

I remember the furniture in the big rooms, the feeling of home and elegance it gave us. Heavy mahogany, damask drapes, thick rugs, even a chess set carved intricately from silken ivory.

Above us, in the small, unheated part of the attic cut into a room, this tall straight-standing woman went to bed at night on a cot, and heated soup over a hot plate, and did alterations for the big store where she once had modeled.

We lived there three years, and I never heard a complaining word from her.

I did hear her say once, "My own fool fault. My husband was a wonderful man and he left me very well fixed. But I thought I had a business head." She shook that crazy hair and the big mouth turned to a grin. "I found out different."

I remember a man of fifty on a city newspaper during the war.

He was kept on by the manager through that sort of hardboiled love which fills all the dirty corners and overlays all of the dusty typewriters in newspapers everywhere. Because once he had been Up There, one of the best, a known byline, and a good guy while he had it.

I remember the way he came in every morning, happy to be dressed and washed and fairly sober, bowing deeply to the women and tossing a gay hand to all of the men.

At nine thirty on the dot, before his first drink of the day, he phoned his mother. "Mama," he called her.

"Mama," he would cry, his voice booming. "See, Mama, I'm all right. Well and happy and all right."

At nine forty-five he would vanish on his first simple assignment. Each time he returned during the day, he moved with greater care. He stopped bowing to the women about two o'clock. He had no wish to fall on his face.

Somewhere along the line, they told me, five or six years earlier, his wife, his son and his baby daughter had died in the fire which destroyed their home.

One night he said to me, thickly, but very sweetly, "Do you know something? Do you know? I say my prayers every night of my life. I don't hurt anybody but myself, do I? He'll realize that, won't He?"

The Fifties.

It would be nice if attaining that age would, or could, mean we were settled and sure and things had quieted down a little and would stay that way.

But they don't. You have seen it, as I have.

Maybe that's what we get for beginning to be reconciled to life, for saying to ourselves, "Well, I had it tough and fought it through, and I deserve this comfortable middle-aged lull and I'm going to enjoy it."

Crazy life.

Never, or almost never, do we relax our vigilance and loosen our grip and trust the whole process completely, but out of the blue comes a hand to upset the apple cart.

Many times it comes in the Fifties.

Sometimes it seems as if life is a series of boxes neatly tied with ambitions or hopes or despair and stored in the attic of the mind, dusty with neglect, but there, each separate and distinct from its fellows.

Babyhood. Kindergarten. School. High School. College. The first job. Courtship. Marriage. Parenthood. Grandparenthood.

Anybody who is fifty or over has packed away these universalities.

As for the world around us, anybody who is fifty or over remembers World War I, the roaring twenties, Black Friday, the Depression, World War II, the years of truce, Korea, the Cold War.

Or in larger boxes still, the Mechanical Age, the Atomic Age, the Space Age.

Quite a time to be born into, the first half or more of the twentieth century, isn't it?

A friend of ours said once, "It seems as if we were young enough for everything and old enough for everything. We came out of school and there was no place for us until we scratched a scrawny sliver of an opening. We just got going, a few steps up, hoping for higher, when we were still young enough to carry a gun or ship out on a carrier or fly a plane."

He shook his head. "And the restlessness afterward. Then, starting again, and my boys growing tall, and Korea." He stopped there for a long time.

"Tell you what," he said abruptly, "I'm glad for one thing, I'm too old now to be sent to the moon."

It can get in your eyes, the dust that blows at fifty.

But, strangely and somehow excitingly, it most often doesn't.

A few years ago an acquaintance of mine, on a bright fall Friday, played nine holes of golf with her husband. She left him then, to play the second nine, while she went home and started preparations for a dinner party they planned to give that evening.

On the seventeenth hole, with no sound at all, her husband died.

On Sunday, she and her three sons sat together in church,

in the balcony where they wouldn't be much noticed, instead of in the pew the five of them had always occupied.

But there. And together. All five together.

In a month she went back to college. Last year she began to teach.

What is it then, that ties all of these small stories together? These, and the many others lying in my mind? And your mind, as you think about it?

It is the quality of the Fifties, the big inner earning of half a hundred years.

It is courage.

It came in small doses, probably. It wasn't always tested to its tautest, thinnest tone, like a violin string tuned too tightly. But day after day, week in and week out, month's end and year's end, life showed what it had to offer. It nibbled or snapped, and sometimes it gouged.

It hurt. But each time it was managed. Time added to time. Small bravery added to bravery.

And courage is cumulative. Finally there is enough, given enough time, given enough living, enough survival.

Well, Fifty has lived. Fifty has survived.

Fifty has a pretty full shelf to start with, and not too much stock has to be ordered.

That is, of course, if Fifty will polish up and keep shining and usable what it already has.

It's very nice at this age if some dreams have come true, some purely practical dreams. It's good to have finished paying for the roof over your head and to see your way clear to retiring in fair comfort ten years from now. It's a satisfaction to know that the children have had adequate educations, have started on interesting jobs, have made you a baby sitter again.

But once again, as in all ages, these are not the greater, deeper satisfactions which bring sound sleep and a good taste in the mind.

There are so many ways of living, all of them as individual as the people who draw breath. Every attitude is as trimly different as leaves on a tree or lines in a face or curves of a body.

But, in general, there are two wide divisions.

Some people live outside-in and other people live inside-out.

If you live outside-in, your contentment and your ecstasy and your plain joy in life are influenced primarily by what happens to you.

When you suffer, you suffer thoroughly, miserably, like an animal, without self-blame.

You are "out of luck." Things "conspire against you." Employers or lovers or friends "do you dirt."

You, yourself, are blameless for outside circumstance. "The cards are stacked." "Lady Luck turns her face away."

If that's the way you are, even when you suffer, it leaves you with a lot.

It leaves you with your ego intact, your self-respect untorn. Even when you get that "dirty deal" you have a little core of righteous enjoyment and self-pity to polish in your mind. Nothing is your fault.

When things go well, if you are an outside-in person, there is no limit to the extraneous material that can bring you joy.

A hot shower, just-right coffee, sunshine, a raise, a good night's sleep, a lavish compliment, any of them can set you up for the day.

The big trouble, of course, is that you live as a child lives.

Your moods sway as quickly, as vulnerably, as simply as a baby's.

It doesn't take much to make you happy, riding the seesaw of emotion. But, conversely, it doesn't take much to make you unhappy either. And both feelings come without warning or control.

If you reach the age of fifty, living always outside-in, the dust blowing in your eyes can blind you for sure. There seem to be so many more things to suffer over than to laugh over.

If you are an inside-out person, everything that happens to you is filtered through the fine sieve of your mind before it has flavor and reality. And that mind can color the grayest of pictures, if it chooses, or dim to darkness the brightest of circumstances.

That mind can nag, too. It hooks onto the somber part of any whole, as well as the gay. It chews both good and bad to digestive size, so that eventually the dark juice, and the bright, become part of your blood stream, your totality.

When your happiness has to come from the *inside* of you outward into the world, you are a battleground of sorts— as a woman in labor is a battleground, riding a force that is bigger than she is, but buoyed always by the knowledge that once she has given birth she will be repaid a thousandfold by the breathing, lasting, growing results of her labor.

When you are an inside-out person of fifty or over, you "have it made," as the youngsters say.

You have picked up your load.

You have carried it strongly.

You have a reserve on which to draw, all that you have lived and thought and felt.

You have resources.

You are realistic.

You have no false pride any more.

You know, most importantly, what counts in the long run and what doesn't, what money can buy and what it can't. You know that half a loaf may not nourish for as long as a whole one, but it is equally sustaining while it lasts.

These are the ingredients which, put together, make up a big shelf of courage.

This is what is meant by that too-slick phrase, "emotional maturity."

It is a phrase which is not to be won in a moment or a decade or in three or four.

It takes a while.

It takes the whole time of your life, the whole time of living.

Emotional maturity is like having glasses made for you which are no longer so finely ground for distance that you cannot see what is right before you in your own hands. Instead, they are glasses which clarify and enlarge and sharpen your vision wherever you look.

And they protect you from any sudden gusts of dust.

☆

CHAPTER ☆ *5* ☆

☆

☆

BORN AGAIN

☆

Once upon a time, there were two prospectors in the middle of the Mojave desert in July.

They came down out of the rock hills in their old car. The miles shimmered ahead of them, alive with heat.

They bumped along the unpaved road which led to the highway, looking forward to the town ten miles away and the small cafe which served hot dinners and cold drinks and was air-cooled.

The old car stopped. It stopped dead and suddenly and for no reason.

They worked on it. For a long time they worked, until they were weak and soaked to their skins and avoiding each other's eyes.

One of them said, "We'll have to walk it. Nobody ever comes up this old road."

The other nodded. He went back to the car and brought

out a clear bottle. It showed a water line neatly in the middle.

He held it up for a terrible, silent moment and licked his lips.

"We'll never make it," he said weakly. "It's ten long miles, and the bottle is half empty."

The other one forced a smile.

"Sure we will," he insisted. "It's only ten miles—and the bottle's not half empty. It's half full. Let's go."

I hate to leave you there. As a matter of fact, I hate to leave the two men there.

I don't know whether they made it or not.

But I'm pretty sure if either one of them made it, which one it was.

It's true in this life that we can't jump from oasis to oasis and ignore the sand.

We can't be forever looking for the silver lining, hunting for the pot of gold at the end of the rainbow, pretending it never stormed.

Over and over again it is proved to us that the very act of drawing breath, of existing, of getting through one year after another, seems sometimes quite beyond our power to manage.

Yet, we do manage.

That is the glory and the power of the human race.

My mother and her best friend are "callers" for the church they attend. It keeps them busy and active. More, it keeps them feeling young.

My mother and her friend, as a matter of fact, are worthy of a thought, a nod, a pat. Having lost their lives, they and so many many others, when they lost their husbands, they have found new lives. Quite simply and with no dramatics,

244

they have discovered all sorts of small things with which to fill their diminishing years.

And they have discovered a few big things. Being "callers" is one of those.

When they go out to make their visits, they go into another world, into the world of the truly old, the amazingly ancient.

Sometimes, when they come back from the rest homes, or the private homes or the hospitals, they are silent and depressed. It takes quite a while for them to get back on an even keel.

Other times they almost sprint into the house, full of a story about a ninety-three-year-old sparking gallantry or an eighty-six-year-old who told them a funny story.

Some of their "old people" they love and look forward to seeing. Others they feel very sorry for, and they try not to drag their heels when they have to go to see them.

My mother and her friend do not attempt to figure out why this is so. They just do the best they can to spread themselves around, and it's good for them that everyone calls them "The Girls."

Listening to their talk, though, I think I have discovered the difference between their two kinds of ancients.

One set wears the years with grace. They wear a cloak, too, as do the young. It is thin, almost lacelike. It does not dance out behind them as they run. Frail as it is, the shallow stir of their breath hardly lifts it.

But the lace is like exquisite hand tatting. It contains many thin, silken threads, enough to make it shine. It is a wrap they have made themselves, something beautiful in which to leave life.

They have created it of remembrance, vague sometimes,

filmily recalled through dim eyes, the slow-moving heart, the slightly confused mind.

They have created it of many things.

Tenderness, adventure, gaiety, innocence. Marriage, understanding, tolerance, responsibility. Patience, compromise, balance, authority, self-control. And the defeat of defeat.

Into this last lovely cloak, those really old have not allowed the memory of the sand and the storm to add any dark threads. They have distilled and purified and looked ahead in serenity.

And the others? The ones whom "The Girls," no matter how great their pity, are reluctant to visit?

They are the ones who have lived it all, too, but have not allowed themselves to look inward.

They are the ones whom no life, however overlong, has been able to teach. Unadjusted, struggling, regretting, everything still unfound, they wear a clumsy, coarse and ill-fitting cloak. They still taste the grit and feel the sting, and the dust stays in their eyes.

And it will stay until they stop breathing.

At that time, at the last breath, they will depart like one of our men in the desert, feeling that the bottle of their life has always been half empty.

The lace-cloaked ones, the trying and hopeful ones who leave life knowing the bottle is half full, as they have known it always, may easily find a joyful surprise in store for them.

They may find that it is a very full vessel, indeed.

THE AUTHOR AND HER BOOK

CHARLOTTE WALRATH EDWARDS, *a native of Erie, Pennsylvania, graduated from the School of Music at Lake Erie College, Painesville, Ohio, in 1931. Having devoted most of her adult life to being a wife and mother, she nonetheless has been a prolific writer because of what she calls "a very demanding typewriter." Her first writing efforts were a weekly music column for the Erie (Pa.) Observer and she later went on to become women's editor of the Rochester (N.Y.) Journal and wrote continuity and women's features for radio station WHEC in Rochester. She later became a reporter and feature writer for the Dayton (O.) Daily News and sold her first piece of fiction—a story called "Beauty's Right," to the Ladies' Home Journal, a magazine to which she has since been a frequent contributor. She has also sold fiction to McCall's, Saturday Evening Post, Good Housekeeping, Cosmopolitan, Woman's Home Companion, Colliers, Woman's Day, Canadian Home Journal, Chatelaine, and Toronto Star Weekly. Using the nom de plume of Vail Edwards, she even had a story published in Argosy. Her short story output is now close to 100 and her previous books are:* **THE RIGHT PLACE FOR LOVE** (*Mc-*

Graw-Hill, *1953*) *and* HEAVEN ON THE DOORSTEP *(Haw-thorn, 1958). She was the writer of two well-known CBS radio programs, Junior Musicomedy and This Is My Land, and several of her short stories have been adapted for television. In recent years she has toured the West Coast doing dramatic readings. She was married to Donald Thomas Edwards, December 15, 1934, in Rochester, N.Y. They have one son, Thomas, and they make their home in Pomona, California.*

HEAVEN IN THE HOME (Hawthorn, 1959) was designed by Sidney Feinberg and completely manufactured by American Book-Stratford Press, Inc. The body type was set on the Linotype in Baskerville, a modern reproduction of the types cut in 1760 by John Baskerville, of Birmingham, England, reflecting the style of stone inscriptions.

A HAWTHORN BOOK

19-302